WOMEN

BOOKS BY THE AUTHOR

Grenadine Etching
I Didn't Know It Was Loaded
One for the Road
Grenadine's Spawn
Horn of the Hunter
Something of Value
The Old Man and the Boy
Poor No More
The Old Man's Boy Grows Older
Uhuru
The Honey Badger
Use Enough Gun
Women

WOMEN

by Robert Ruark

Edited by Joan Fulton

THE NEW AMERICAN LIBRARY

First Printing

Published by The New American Library, Inc.
1301 Avenue of the Americas, New York, New York 10019
Published simultaneously in Canada
by General Publishing Company, Ltd.
Library of Congress Catalog Card Number: 67-27437
Printed in the United States of America

"I like women—because some of them are so pretty, and a few are intelligent enough to appreciate me."

Robert Ruark

Contents

Introduction

Robert Ruark lived his life loving and hating women at one and the same time. He had a small-boy quality of worship for the beautiful female, and a romantic, almost antebellum, attitude toward any one of them he wanted to see more than once.

He sent roses — they were always red roses — not consciously as a lure, but out of a sense of gallantry, as a gesture of admiration.

He had a way of making the woman at his side feel that she was the only one in his life, and if his Southern chivalry was sometimes lost to the less courtly use of terms like "broad" and "dame" and "chum" as friendship blossomed, it was accompanied by such camaraderie that no woman could be offended.

Each in turn had to discover that he could love her always but live with her hardly ever.

The only girl who captivated him enough to last something more than twenty years as his wife was the late Virginia Webb Ruark. For one thing, she never came between him and his typewriter, although she provided a lot of material for it. Anyone who tried to keep him from that old, faithful, beaten-up keyboard was in for a short run. And the roses stopped coming.

The women in his fiction are beautiful, talented, witty, and adorable; they are whistle bait. That is the way women, for him, should be. In reality, with few exceptions, they disappointed him, and he never ceased to rail at their clothes, their hairdos and makeup, their querulousness, and their demoniac domination over, in his words, the poor suffering male.

He embraced women, then, on two planes, Fact and Fiction. The gap between them is there to see, although it could be that the heroines of his stories were drawn from a combination of the real thing and the way he would like it to have been.

Somewhere between the hard Fact and the softer Fiction, his imagination led him to play a few tricks and Fantasy found its way into his writing.

All three are included in this collection.

— Joan Fulton

WOMEN

PART ONE

My War With Women

I

Women started giving me trouble at a very early age.

My first recallable brush with the opposite sex was a difference of opinion with my mother, a lady who had very strong ideas about the conduct of young gentlemen of less than voting age. She did not believe in constant corporal punishment, but was an advocate of the house-arrest school of punitive therapy. I was an active sprout, but it seems I spent most of my early life in bed. This is a possible explanation of why I have since found it so difficult to retire before dawn. Ma substituted mandatory retirement for the castor-oil-and-hickory-switch method of reform.

The first real encounter with the indomitable power of a woman occurred when I was somewhere in the vicinity of six. A demon of a child named Wendell Newton — his name is etched in flames on my memory — laid siege to Grandpa's house in Southport, North Carolina, and attacked me evilly and successfully every time I ventured outside the protection of the palinged portcullis, or garden gate.

It was very simple. Wendell would crouch in ambush. I would attempt to operate in a free world. He would attack. He would hit me. I would weep, and flee to sanctuary behind the fence. He would laugh, and I would cry.

This simple experiment in human relations was noted by my dam, a large, fearless female who rode horses astride when more decorous damsels rode sidesaddle and fainted at the sight of mice. One day, when Wendell Newton had reduced me to a sobbing wreck of lumped eyes and abject fear, the good woman who bore me met me at the gate with a stout stick. This stick she proceeded to apply to my rear end, laying it on with what seemed unnecessary vehemence. It hurt. It hurt worse than Wendell. This woman was killing me — me, a wounded man from an earlier war.

"And," she said, as she bestowed another hearty blow with the stave, "I shall continue to beat you with this stick, my brave bucko, every time you run away from Wendell Newton. If you think he can hurt you, you have observed nothing yet in the way of pain. Take that, you coward, and make up your own mind."

I was a logical little cuss, and it seemed to me that if the price, computed in pure pain, of running away from Wendell became more inflated when I encountered an unnatural mother, then the best thing to do was not to run away from Wendell. So I reversed my tactics.

The next time I ventured out, the monster came at me,

and instead of running or covering up, I clouted him on the chin. He went over, as fully surprised as I. He got up and I sloughed him again. Bong! Down he went. So I landed atop him, and was very busy pounding his skull into the sidewalk when Mother arrived and peeled me off him. He ran away, sobbing, and never bothered me again.

Ma congratulated me for my fresh-found bravery. Then she got out the lath and paddled me once more. "This," she said, "is to teach you not to hit people when they cannot defend themselves."

I retired to my tree house (I was Tarzan of the Apes at the time, until supper call) and reflected on the mysterious blessing with which God endowed us: women. I have been reflecting morosely ever since, and have come to only one concrete answer: We are in a battle to the death with women, and must get there first with the most, or we are lost.

This constant battle has afforded me a very pleasant living. For, as the watchdog of women, in behalf of man, I have made a career out of keeping them at least partially in their place.

Actually, I am in favor of hitting girls when they deserve it, but an ingrained fear of scratching and hair-pulling, apart from a social code which makes woman-striking unchic, prevents the average man from administering the first blow. I have fined it down to what is known generally as Ruark's Rule: Do not strike them until struck first. This combines chivalry with practicality, because any delicate creature who takes a gratuitous swing at a guy is just begging for a bruised lip.

A pretty little girl named Mary Black Bolles (with the

most sadistic set of reflexes I ever encountered, even among bigger girls) was basically responsible for Ruark's Rule. She had a very high front porch. She used to push me off it until I was a basket case from one month's end to the other. One day, reason glimmered in my skull. I pushed Mary Black off her own front porch, and she ceased pushing me off the front porch. I understand she reformed her habits, married well, and is now a society matron with children who probably push each other off the front porch, to their mother's consternation.

After the first horror of Mother and Mary Black had partially worn off, I ventured among the world of women and fell in love, at the age of seven, with a dreadful little girl named Martha Moore. This awful event occurred at dancing school, or some such, and led to a veritable orgy of movies and ice-cream sodas, during which I learned of the grasping greed, the naked rapaciousness of the female for material things. I also learned that all women — even six-year-old women — are perpetually hungry, petulant, and starved for entertainment. And that they expect man to provide satisfaction for all three moods.

By the time I was ten, I was a bitterly disillusioned man, I can tell you. The background of general distrust has lingered since, richened and ripened by romance and a marriage which has endured for many years, most of which have found me on the defensive.

It is hard to say at what age a man first begins to study women seriously, for the odd beasts that really they are. It seems to me that a fruitless fixation for a redheaded schoolteacher afflicted me at fourteen, and a bootless love affair involving a blonde with dimples beset me at fifteen, suggesting suicide when she became hopelessly enamored of both my best friends. This taught me that women are apt to be fickle.

I fought through the Chi Omega and Pi Phi houses at the University of North Carolina in Chapel Hill, accruing heart scars all the way, but literally found my way into a career among the arts when spring infected me with a hopeless passion for a journalism student. Enough knowledge rubbed off to qualify me for the job of copy boy. She married a doctor.

After a brief interlude involving two Russian female sailors in Hamburg, Germany — I never did know which I loved the best, but both said *"Da"* to everything — I encountered the first and only fatal instance of the true guile of the female, woman-type girl. I wound up in Washington, D.C., busted and hungry. I met a dame with an icebox. Taking advantage of my physical weakness, she fed me — not much, but enough to lead me on and lure me into her terrain. This woman I married, more from hunger than otherwise.

It took me years of Blondie-Dagwood marital punishment, and considerable cauliflowering of the soul as well as ears, to solve the riddle of women, which I will impart to the gentlemen readers later on for no extra charge. But at the end of, shall we say, ten years, I had received my doctorate in dames. If one lives in the same cage with a tiger long enough, one eventually learns one hell of a lot about tigers.

During the war, since I was almost perpetually attached to lonesome ships and chained to lonelier islands, I had considerable opportunity to dwell upon dames and their place in our time. This was pretty simple, really, because there were no dames around on these ships and these islands to distract me from my thoughts about dames.

I concluded some basic things about women, including the fact that they served a purpose and were apt to be around for some time. Then I started looking for a way to live off them, in a clean sort of fashion not involving the moral outlook of a paid escort, and suddenly I hit it. I hit it one night off Espiritu Santo, in the New Hebrides, when I was unable to sleep due to fear, or something.

"Vanity!" I said, startling the helmsman considerably. "Eureka! Vanity is the key."

"What was that, sir?" the helmsman asked in the gloom. "You gettin' rock-happy on me?"

"Never you mind," said I. "This is too good for the enlisted personnel. Watch your course. You steer this ship like a lady walks."

"I wish I steered the old bag that good," the helmsman said, heaving a sigh. He also solidified my resolve.

What had come to me in the beautiful womanless Pacific night was a simple thing, to wit: Some women are pretty, some are ugly, some are young, some are old, some are fat, and some are thin. But they're all vain. And they are all extremely sensitive to criticism. And they have no sense of humor when it concerns themselves. And they all react out loud.

Some months later the nice man who was making out my Navy discharge papers asked idly, "What are you going to do now you're out, mister?"

"Sir," I said, loud and strong, "I am faring forth to prey on women."

He eyed me rather oddly as I left, whistling.

People still say, after all these years: "I remember that first piece of yours—that piece you wrote about women's clothes, just after you got back from the war." My poor friends, that was no story about women's clothes. That was a master chunk of cerebration based on the simple and beautiful logic of people. That was a signpost to a life of opulence. That was the guidebook to King Solomon's Mines, for, behold, it has enabled me to live without work, and I owe it all to woman.

When a guy comes home to write after years at the wars, he wishes to hurl the very largest stone he can find through the most vulnerable greenhouse on the horizon. I debated for some weeks before I wrote the first column of the postwar. My reasoning ran thus:

"The whole purpose of winning a war is to get John back with Mary. Mary has been here, John has been there. The war ends, and John comes home from across the seas. Mary meets him at the boat. They rush into each other's arms with glad cries. They retire to the cozy nook with the mortgage and live happily ever after, amidst a welter of children and unpaid bills.

"What would happen (I asked me) if John came home and took one look at Mary and said, in horror, 'My God! What is this awful creature I see before me? I had it better in Funafuti, and when does the next boat leave?' "

So that is what I wrote. In a chaste little piece which, oddly, made the newspaper front pages, I suggested that the American woman, as she met the American G.I., was the most ridiculous-looking thing that ever affronted the eye of man. This was no fashion piece. This was a piece on S*E*X, and the rejection of same by the male — a horrible insult to female vanity. Take a look and see if it ain't so; this is it.

As I have been since Boy Scout days an ardent admirer of American female beauty, I am pained, as a returned serviceman, to discover I have been dead wrong.

American women today are very curious-looking critters — they seem to have sabotaged themselves.

During the tough months in Funafuti or Peleliu, one of the things which made foxholes, K rations, and dysentery bearable was the thought that someday we would come home, and there would be wonderful American women.

So every day batches of us return. So what do we find? What we find shouldn't happen to a war criminal.

Our girls, who kept our souls alight when we were sleeping in mud or being ill on destroyers, look like something Salvador Dali might muster up after a midnight snack of Welsh rabbit.

That lovely hair we remembered curling sweetly about our ladies' shoulders; it has been tortured into two patterns, both repulsive. Either it has been snatched up in one pink fist, hauled taut with a windlass, and screwed into a silly topknot; or else it is clubbed into a nauseous bundle and hangs down the neck like a sackful of mud, or maybe a beaver's tail.

Now, this is all wrong, girls. You are providing no change for us men who've been in the Pacific. The native girls in the Admiralties arrange their locks likewise. They pin their crests with shells, feathers, and Grandpa's shinbone. They manage to look just like Miss Firehouse No. 3, who strangles her tresses with a rubber band and crams the overflow full of flowers, beads, and bric-a-brac.

As for this business of dumping the hair into a crocus sack and letting it flap soggily down the nape, our dolls are missing a couple of tricks. As any Melanesian belle can tell you, a similar but more enduring hairdo may be achieved by daubing the strands with rancid cocoa butter and mud. Chief difference between this and the Stateside cutie's locks, lathered with fixative unguents, is that it is easier to stand downwind from our dames.

And I used to remember fondly the American girl's walk.

That long, free stride that made them look tall and slim and proud. What I see now makes me long for the Ubangi country.

Our dames crowd their feet into spiked shoes that make them totter like unreconstructed Chinese women. Or they slop around in heelless ballet slippers that endow their walk with all the winsome grace of an Okinawa coolie. Or they struggle along in built-up brogans which give the impression that the wearer is either club-footed or has just trudged through a Georgia clay pit.

On Sono Osato, ballet slippers look good, but on you, honey, they just look flat-footed.

What's more, it makes your legs look like milk bottles, or maybe the only women who wear ballet shoes on the street just naturally have legs which look like milk bottles.

When God made little girls and little boys he made the little boys wide on top and narrow at the bottom, and the girls vice versa. So it is shocking to observe the trend in ladies' suits, shoulders padded so that the slightest of females resembles a professional football player in battle dress. The bulky shoulder, plus an atrocity called the dolman sleeve, currently transforms a ninety-pound sylph into lady wrestler.

Of purple lipstick and four-inch fingernails I will say nothing, except that Arab ladies sometimes tattoo their lips purple and Australian aborigines leave their nails long for purposes of scratching those parasites of the order Siphunculata.

And hats? A hat is a spittoon, is a hood, is an ashtray, is a bundle of laundry, is a hat. I have seen handsomer headdresses on cannibals.

It won't be surprising if the boys start remembering Australia, England, and even Germany overfondly. Over there at least the women look like women.

Hanged if I know what our girls do look like, but whatever it is, 'tain't what we left behind in '42.

The story smote the country with the crash of an elephant stumbling into a skylight. In a week's time I was a black beast to 80 percent of the nation's female population. I got 22,000 letters in one week, almost all of which contained pictures. The letters said: "What you say of all the other girls may be perfectly true, but this does not apply to me. I enclose photograph. . . ."

Friends, I knew I was home. This was the trick the ancient alchemists sought and never found. I had finally fetched up with a better mousetrap, and an endless gold mine of nothing more involved than females and female vanity. In a few weeks, after a couple of half-passes yielded an avalanche of response, my poor employers could do nothing less than write me a contract assuring me freedom from real toil, forever.

To understand the American woman you have to go back a bit. You must remember that the female's ascendance to mastery in this nation was based on the original shortage of female people in the country. A premium was placed upon the lady because she existed in such small supply. This created a tyranny of fear, as all shortages create tyrannies. The fear was based on the fact that if Papa did not behave Mama would go away, and there would be no more fluffy ruffles in the closet.

The foundation on fear in the American home instilled a few succinct rules for living. Here they are: Mama is right; Papa is wrong. Mama is basically good; Papa is basically bad. Mama leaves Papa if Papa is real naughty. Papa cannot leave Mama without being esteemed a cad and a bounder and paying through the nose for the privilege.

Ergo: Mama controls the purse strings. Mama reserves the right to raise hell. The hand that rocks the cradle rules the world. Papa goes about the business of living with his heart's delight with a built-in complex.

Furthermore: Woman starts with an entirely spurious mystery, involving the ancient bit about what little girls and little boys are made of. It is my claim that boys are not of necessity composed of nails, snails, and puppy dog tails. There have been times when I felt myself to be completely compounded of sugar, spice, and everything nice, while that gal who sits glowering in the corner clanks when she walks, due to the constant inner concussion of snails and nails.

We might have perpetuated the female myth if she had been content to lie back and revel in her semi-godhood. Instead, she has insisted on topping the male animal in recent years, or at least in striving to run a dead heat with him, whilst still endeavoring to maintain all the dewy little fictions of poor weak womanhood.

She spot-welds for overtime pay, and expects her man friend to buy the sodas. She runs for Congress, and becomes furious when doors are not opened and handkerchiefs are not speedily collected when she drops them. She has wanted it all — the right to smoke cigars, wear pants, and be President, while furiously defending her right to weep, scream, faint, collect alimony, and be protected. Something had to give, or else we live in a perpetual powder room of matriarchal society, with the strength sapped from the menfolk and the women running the world.

It pleases me to report that recent medical researches show the female to be suffering at least as much as males, and possibly more, from duodenal ulcer. Up to a few years ago the stomach ulcer was unknown in women. Ulcers are caused from nerves — worry over jobs, insecurity, high daily tension. It was not until the lady nominated herself for masculine office that she developed a perforation of the stomach lining. She now has a bigger and better ulcer than Daddy has. Wear your badge of emancipation proudly, ladies, and pick up your own gloves.

Anyone who has lived around women any length of time knows that no horse is so strong as a ninety-pound female. She stands cold better than men, and bears up better under heat. Illnesses that would send a man to his grave barely dent the outer composure of the woman. I do not believe the strongest man in the world could face the chore of bearing a baby. The women do it all the time. No male brain is so hard as the brain of woman — no will so steely, no purpose so unspecked by scruple.

But the gals have been trying to perpetuate the myth of fluffy weakness and vaporous helplessness, and have suddenly become annoyed when some irreverent, such as me, tells them about it.

Women scream in anger when you tell them to knock off all the business of props to femininity, such as falsies, and they are outraged when you refer to the female chest purely as costume jewelry. Yet the American woman's mammary glands have entered into the public domain so fully that industries are founded on brassiere measurements, and television flourishes thereby.

There is about as much mystery in the modern woman today as there is to a glass of water. Advertising has robbed her of all the little tricks she has used to snare the male. I can tell you, in terms of whalebone, elastic, foam rubber, snaps, hair dyes, lip rouge, eye shadow, permanent waves, deodorants, creams, polishes, powders, restrainers, exaggerators, and depilatories exactly what the exquisite femme fatale is made of. She is an odd hybrid of drugstore, civil engineering, and fashionable whim.

The two things that women cannot abide are to be (1) understood and (2) laughed at. A female divested of her little props to domination is a very helpless creature, subject to sudden tears. A woman laughed at is twice as deadly as the woman scorned, because when you can laugh at her you are no longer afraid of her, and she knows it.

Tears — to dissolve the man into helplessness — have always comprised the woman's readiest weapon when she wishes to prove a point. There are two ways to cope with tears: You either ignore them, as you ignore the slammed door and the threat to go-home-to-Mother, or else you learn to cry yourself. I spent considerable time on this trick, and now am able to burst into as noisy a spate of weeps as was ever committed by a female for shock effect. Crying as a pressure device has ceased in my house since I learned how to unleash the tear ducts. There is no point in two people weeping at each other.

Girls were always too big for their britches, because God made girls that way, and never intended them for either spiritual or actual slacks. A girl in pants is a ridiculous thing, whether they are pants of the cloth or pants of the mind. But until I (he says modestly) and a few other disciples came along, the dames were actually beginning to believe that they were not broad where broads should be broad, but might interchange the filmy tulle of femininity for the harsh tweed trousers of masculine prerogative. They believed they could slide from the role of masculine competitor to their old estate of winsome wenchery without damage. In this they were wrong, because you do not kiss the lady executive who just did you in the eye on a business deal, or who defeated you for public office.

When milady abandons her role as global politician, master of the office, and lord of the home to go weak and alluring in the presence of the male, she is pretty funny.

Her wiles are as transparent as her motive, which can be seen through from five miles away on a foggy day. The completely phony intentness on what the "dreat bid mans" is saying; the accidental brush of the body; the quick pressure of the hand; the downcast eye and the batted eyelash; the slavish admiration; the ever constant yes; the coy withdrawal; the drench of scent; the daring gown; the general presentation of all-this-for-only-you attitude — oh, sister, come out from behind all those gimmicks. You are really a stevedore in Schiaparelli clothing, and what goes on in that steel-trap mind would frighten a psychiatrist. And don't wave that neckline at me, honey.

But you must not forget my professional stock-in-trade, which is that vanity thing. You can laugh at her, you can kid the literal pants off her, you can sneer at her foibles and scorn her fashions and jest at her transparency and condemn her militances. But she is so wonderfully conceited that she firmly refuses to believe you are talking about her — she herself — in person. You must mean all the other girls, because she's different. And so she climbs a pinnacle of scorn for all the other poor women who have aroused your displeasure. I say "displeasure," because the trick in handling women is never to allow them the satisfaction of actually incurring wrath. They can handle anger, gusty fury. They are helpless before mild, amused displeasure, because there is nothing in the book to tell them how to cope with it.

And they are susceptible to praise. You can batter their brains out for months, and then drop them one little sop of sympathy or applause — purely spurious, as false as some of their facades — and they will forgive you. Just pat them gently once in a while, and tell them they have good babies and are occasionally nice to look at if no other scenery is handy, and they will wriggle under your hand like happy puppies. There again is vanity; a woman will believe anything nice you say about her, as she stoutly disbelieves anything derogatory.

You will run into exceptions, of course. At one time, three hundred old ladies in a home for the aged informed me by daily bulletin that they were engaged in praying me to death, and by direct voodoo induced so many concurring accidents and minor tragedies in my life that I had to ask them to knock off. I was flying a lot in those days, and this punishment by prayer didn't seem fair to the other passengers. By mail and by mouth, a minority of clients have intimated that I was a cad, a bounder, a heel, a wife-beater, a wizened old man, a fat old eunuch, and a scandal. Some have intimated that I hate women, which is not so. I do not hate them. I love them. It is just that I am not impressed with women as women per se or as a superior social force. I think them subject to foible, even as man.

In my crusades to keep women from running away with the world, lock, stock, and compact, I have been slapped, slugged with pocketbooks, sworn at, and, occasionally, been forced to duck a hurled glass from a lady who temporarily forgot that all women are ladies. But the mail has also brought proposals of marriage from strangers, and, oddly enough, my dance card seems to be generally well filled.

To sum, I would say that the only hope of mankind is to fight women, if not with fists, with words and ideas. We must fight them in the restaurants and in the homes and through the newspapers and on the beaches and in the beauty shops. We must never relax, and we must never admit to more than a 50 percent error in our relations with them. We must disabuse them of the idea of invincibility and of earthly godhood, because demigoddesses they ain't.

We must be firm with them at all times, and gentle when possible, but must also remember that a hurled slipper or roundhouse right must be repaid in kind. We must be tolerant of them in their little sins of sloth around the house, and we must continually remind them of the respect due a man who comes wearily home from the rope walk and who does not need a six-round fight to whet his appetite for a badly cooked dinner, despite all modern devices of canned food and shortcut cookery.

Above all, we must be firm with wives. Wives get out of hand much more easily than other women, due to some misplaced concept of permanence, despite frizzled hair and cold-creamed faces. And speaking of wives reminds me that I am smuggling this document out of the house. My bride beats me when I talk ugly about girls.

II

The other day my good woman was standing in front of the mirror, taking a long, searching look at herself. She was wearing a box, a kind of cloth coffin. It was about as high up the style ladder as you could climb. A Balenciaga, yet. She looked like a wrestler. I did not say anything, not being that stupid.

"Damn and blast and *mucho* unprint," she said. "I am unprint and more unprint tired of being stylish and ugly. And I am ugly in this Balenciaga mess. I was ugly in Christian Dior, and I was uglier in Jacques Fath. What the unprint is the point of being stylish if all you are is ugly?"

Now, all you people who know and love me are going to appreciate the fact that I didn't charge into this fray. Said I:

"Even ugly, I think you're pretty," or some such. Actually, she looked like the wrath of God. She had on a pregnant lady's coat down to her knees, and a skinny skirt that was shorter than the flappers used to wear. And this, friends, was haut couture, at what cost I wouldn't care to consider.

"I got some hips, and you can't see 'em," the disenchanted maiden continued. "I have a waist, and you can't see it. They've hung a belt on this thing that is so low-slung I feel like I'm wearing a diaper. I am not the sheath-gown type, and from now on I start a one-woman rebellion. I'm going to hire a dressmaker and start wearing clothes that'll make me feel like a girl again, instead of a fashionable mess."

"It says here in *Vogue* —" I ventured.

"Start the fire with *Vogue*," she snapped. "And use *Esquire* for the extra kindling. American men look nearly as silly as American women ever since they started that new 'narrow look.' You can see more silly-looking guys around New York than I ever remember. Look at the hats they're wearing, and the caps. And those hairdos!"

"Yes, ma'am," I said. "But if you will notice the battered plumage of your mate, here, the brims are still wide, and the hat crowns are still pinched, and you can still find a lapel on my coats. No cap has ever crowned my locks, which have been allowed to remain in sparse splendor to give a little *je ne sais quoi* to my ears.

"I may be corny, but I attract no undue attention in Rome, Italy, or London, England, or Barcelona, Spain, which is where most of my finery leaves the tailor's shears. So I will continue to be regarded as a freak in New York."

"You look like a riverboat gambler in that black Homburg," she said waspishly.

"Very well," said I. "I paid fifty dollars for this black Homburg to the Cavanagh boys ten years ago, and I would rather look like a riverboat gambler than these pinheads you see with the two-inch brims with the bows in back. A man with my kind of ears needs a hat brim on top. Also I ain't no college boy to pick up every fad that comes along. Nor do I want to look like Madison Avenue."

"You haven't changed a suit style in the twenty years I've had custody of you," she came back with, "except for that little blue number with the gold buttons the Navy hung on you."

"And I expect to continue," said I. "I am not a wishy-washy woman, swayed annually by whims of some sissy boy in Paris whose main idea is to make women look uglier whilst making money as well. When I attire myself in garments, I am not heading for a costume party. *Madame,* you are married to a square."

"For the first time in nearly twenty years we find ourselves in complete agreement," the crown of thorns replied. "But I think, in all fairness, I may join your team and go back to looking like a woman again, instead of a Paris-created freak."

The next day she had nipped in the waistline, removed a few bows and belts, and I swear you wouldn't know it was the same dame. Now, at least, you could tell it was a dame, instead of a zombie in a tow sack.

But the breakthrough is short-lived. I mean when they're not trying to look like an inflated space man or one of those tanks that kept Stalingrad from the Germans they find other ways to fray a man's nerves and decimate his pocketbook.

It is very possible that one pair of women's shoes employs less material by weight than a small spider web, but we have always paid horrible prices for these wisps of leather with the toes chewed out and the heels bare.

With the exception of the chain mail to hold in the hips, and the dead minks the wealthier wenches sport, the average material in female frippery is about one-tenth of the average men's wear. We have always been told that the extra cost of feminine clothes was due to the intricate styling and the changing mode. We paid and kept mouths shut.

I am about to widen my big yap. The burr in my blanket

rolled in — how else? — with a bundle and opened it with some pleasure.

"What's that?" sezzi. "Shirts," she answers. "Thanks very much," sezzi. "They're beautiful." "I know it," says she, "but they're not for you. They're for me."

Now here is a dozen shirts, with men's sleeves and men's collars and men's shirttails. Exactly what you'd see in *Esquire* for the well-dressed gent. I asked the cost. Two bucks more than I pay for mine, per each, although the shirts aren't any bigger than boy size.

I have noticed that this lady goes to a man's tailor for her slacks, and he charges her more than he charges me. In this case I guess the overcharge is worth it, because a dame consumes more material in the seat than a man does.

But the moccasin shoes she wears are cut on a man's last, and the sweaters are mannish, and so are the shorts, and so are the sports coats. She even goes to the haberdashery now and buys neckties to wear with her new pink shirts. And steals my cuff links.

This is all right. If a dame wants to look like a man — up to haggling off her hair — fine.

I am merely sore about paying for men's clothes on a female chassis — and paying more for the clothes than I pay for mine, when I use up ten times the leather and three times the material. They can't say I'm buying style now, because the style is man-style, accepted, tooled for production for years, and completely without female innovation. Hers is merely a lot smaller.

It should cost a lot less. I know small men today who still dress cheaply by buying boy-size clothes. Always a youngster's suit or shoes cost less than full-sized adult wear. But the dames are buying small-boys' clothes and paying more than are big men.

I claim this is pure fraud. The stylists have made such a horrible example of the old lady as a sucker that the swindle continues even when Mama is preening men's plumage. You can't tell me that a simple pair of dungarees is supposed to cost more just because a woman bags 'em in the seat.

I do not attempt to revise the thinking that makes a female a chump, or the male thinking that allows the man to applaud stupidity in the woman. But I just want to get it on the record that nobody's fooling nobody.

When anniversary time comes around, I am going to give my lass a fine present. I have found a cheap tailor. I have swiped her measurements.

What she gets from me will be a lot of old clothes — cut-down shirts, sawed-off pants, old naval suntans, and a couple of shrunken sweaters. It is exactly what she's paying a ransom for at the moment, and if she's got to turn herself into a boy, I aim to see she does it cheap. Including the haircut, which I will administer myself.

Not only that. I have devised a masterful stratagem when it comes to less than delight of m'lady's latest fad, and I am moved to present a public service, which comes with no surcharge.

Gentlemen all, I got my old lady in a state of collapse, nervewise, and I wish to pass on a few handy little tricks to help us win the battle of the year. All you need in this do-it-yourself warfare is a copy of *Vogue* and a little malicious thought.

First you strike her, psychologically, sharply below the

belt. When she is bulging in spots where ladies normally bear a burden described as "a delicate condition," you kiss her tenderly and ask innocently when she expects it.

If she says don't be silly, then suggest — mildly — that perhaps she had better lose a little weight. When she says profanely that she's lost weight, murmur: "Maybe it's the dress, darling." This'll fetch 'em every time.

Hitting below the belt is very necessary to the campaign. I have enjoyed tremendous success with the belt bit. If the belt is hiked up under her chins (plural), just say it looks fine until she sits down and then suddenly seems to cause her excess weight to hang over her girdle.

If the belt is behind the behind, tell her it exaggerates the lines in her face — sort of depressed and dragged out. Or that for the first time you realize that she was broader in the beam than you thought when you offered wedded bliss. The belt points up what can only be called a generous sitz-platz.

I find, as a warm-up pitch, you can offer a blanket criticism. Tell her the sack dress is lovely because it reminds you of your mother. "But," you say sweetly, "my mother was younger then."

Of course the skirt is too short, but you don't want to act up nasty. Vulgarity never pays. What you say is this: "Sweetie, you know I never realized before how many knock-kneed and bowlegged people there are around these days — how many piano-legged, fat-ankled, skinny-legged girls there are in the world. You'd think, with all these vitamins. . . ."

When the dress she just hocked the Cadillac to buy reminds you of nothing so much as an elephant's hind quarters, you compliment her on her "new coat." When she explains that it isn't a coat but a dress, you ask her where it unbuttons and express naïve amazement that it is a dress at all.

As for the forward slouch that goes with this perversion of woman's natural assets, you can really skull 'em with the solicitous statement that they see a doctor — that they seem to have a dislocated spine and an X ray is indicated. Refrain from the mad desire to give them a boot in the tail to straighten them out. It takes a gentleman to win this argument.

If she has succumbed to the filled-in look, which means no neckline whatsoever, and has taken to raiding the five-and-dime for bogus adornment, such as ten-cent pearls, glass diamonds, bottle tops, and similar clutter, just show her a picture of a Ubangi maid and bring her home a facsimile of the soup plates the African devotees to the local *Vogue* wear in their lips to make them look like ducks. And add somebody's old shinbone to thrust through the septum.

Oh, gentlemen, there are masses of goodies I haven't touched on to help us win this war against horrible female adornment, but the skimpy ones I offer here are at least sufficient to reform the French fashion boys, and more than adequate to buy you a sort of home-permanent divorce.

III

A woman, according to the ancient concept, is a mysterious critter molded by God in a divine form which differs from man in a pleasant and beguiling fashion, and who was put here for the mutual convenience of both man and woman, with an eye to the perpetuation of the race and some simultaneous aid and comfort to each other.

Over the years we worked up some clichés, or standards, by which man approached woman, and vice versa.

Women were mysterious in mind and body.

Women comprised the weaker sex.

Women were created to be fed, watered, and cherished by man, in return for which they bore his children, mended his shirts, and succored him in his hour of emotional or physical need. At one time there was even a clause in the marital contract which said that the lady promised to love, honor, and obey. The years have shown this to be a spurious promise.

Women wept when unhappy. Men did not.

Women were to be protected, and honored, and even worshiped, as a commodity only slightly less base than the angels, but a considerable cut loftier than man.

Women had bosoms and legs which were desirable in the sight of man, as a symbol of woman's elusive monopoly, but which must not be flagrantly flaunted for fear of blunting her appeal.

Nice girls did not chase men.

Wives ran the home. Husbands supplied the bacon.

Boys cut their hair short. Women wore their locks long. Hair was referred to as "woman's crowning glory."

Women dressed alluringly, in order to show off their best points and minimize their worst.

There was ever a clearly defined separation of the sexes. Papa worked in the rope walk; Mama sweated over a hot cookstove. Papa had to shave every day; Mama had her own private periodic troubles. Man complemented woman, in a neat little way that the Lord thought up in a moment of undeniable genius, and everybody was preordained to dwell happily ever after.

And then, of a sudden, woman began to inspect herself, to become dissatisfied with her obvious inadequacies, to fret about her faults, to cast an envious eye at her mate, or her probably mate, and to climb outside her ken. In her uneasy self-assertion, she finally has caricatured her sex, to the dismay of man and the ruination of her specialty, which is being unmale.

Let us look at her prime stock-in-trade, the mystery of femininity. This was the big seller in the marts of matrimony — *mystery*. "I am a little girl," the copybook said. "I am a bundle of sugar and spice and other delectable condiments, and I am shaped different, and I react different, and to get to know me well — to investigate this Pandora's box of goodies — you better come a-running with a preacher and a diamond ring and an apartment, and then, oh, boy!"

It was assumed that this boon eventually, after the ceremony and the rice, would catch Wilbur up on all he didn't know about girls, including the fact that they were built differently and delightfully. This was bait, pure and simple: *marry me, darling, and learn about women.* Lingerie, for instance, once was a sexy word, because that is what women called their underwear. Time was when an exposed instep had some glamor — later on, a sneaked peek at a knee-cap was supposed to be thrillful. All the secrets of femininity — hairdo, perfume, makeup, clothes — were on the distaff security list, which was jealously guarded by the guild.

Suppose we inspect the little tricks Grandma used to practice quietly in the all-out effort to drop the noose on a perpetual meal ticket. Call it modesty. Call it restraint. Call it good taste. And remember that Grandma, too, had bosoms, and wore pants, of a sort, and cheated a little in minimizing the bad and emphasizing the good.

We have become so surfeited today with the intimate details of what used to be called feminine secrets that I fear for the fate of romance. There is simply nothing left that you don't know about ladies.

There was a time when what a lady wore beneath her dimity was her own business, and all true gentlemen assumed that she was perfect of form and divine in figure. If she remodeled a little deficiency here with subterfuge, or tamped down a rebellious curve, that was a secret between her and the mirror until she lassoed her sucker. One never referred to a lady's pants in public. One did not even speculate as to whether she wore same, for legend said that all nice girls did, if only in fear of accident.

This reticence was rather charming, in that it allowed all hands to delude themselves that there weren't *any* ladies whose form was less fabulous, or who needed an engineering project to enhance and limit and protect and control their more salient abutments. Now one begins to speculate, after a steady diet of girdles and pants and bras and pantie girdles in the journals, as to whether there are any ladies left who are not in need of an expensive shoring-up process — if there are any women whose charm is theirs alone and not a testament to the nylon-and-elastic industries.

I am old enough to recall an era when the normal development of female pectoral muscles was regarded as functional, and not as a focus for ad writers, movie moguls, chatter columnists and TV and radio gagmen. The merchandisers have finally robbed Mama of her mystery in the upper hemisphere, to where the bo-zoom is as much a part of your daily reading life as any cereal ad. Winsome child that I am, I can now speak freely of falsies, half-cups, uplifts, separations, cleavages, and plunging necklines. Breasts became a stout topic of ideological conversation in the television industry, with the point predicated on whether the girls were swooping too low for the national health. I know about A, B, C, and D cups, wiring, padding, strapless brassieres, and all of the saucy trade names like Bosom Friend. I know all about these things because I read about them daily in the magazines and newspapers.

I have also become an involuntary expert on falsies, a triumph of modern engineering designed to make mountains of molehills. Grandma may have padded her off-the-shoulder frock with a few fluffy ruffles, but you can bet your life Grandpa was not exposed to the fraud until Granny had him cornered.

Every effort in recent years has been made to reduce the lady fair to her component parts of sham. It has largely been the fault of the eager hucksters who play the pale green typewriters, but the lady has lapped up the effort and eagerly cooperated in her own downfall. I am led to believe today that no woman can hold a man a minute unless she paints on her eyes with Glo-Goo, the Unguent of the Ancient Nile. She is bound to smell bad without liberal application of Whiff-Oh-No, the dainty deodorant of the debs. Her face belongs not to her, nor to the angels, but to Madame Du Barry or the Du Pont laboratories. Love flees her next because she refuses to use the right laxative.

The net effect on man is one of horror. Since everything from laxative to tooth powder is nakedly designed to seduce him, as castor powder is used to smear beaver traps, he is apt to disregard the lure and see only the trap. The entire assault is so tasteless and shameless that the basic woman seems merely an angular hat rack, festooned and smothered and cluttered with all kinds of gimmicks and gadgets, every one of them designed to make her appear as something that she is not.

The perfume industry has sinned rather violently in reducing the dame to the ridiculous. If one absorbs enough ultraviolent copy, in the sale of high-pressured foo-foo ointments, one easily gathers the impression that a well-scrubbed girl is slow afoot in the matrimonial sweepstakes. She must daub herself with so much orgy oil that, evidently, the quarry faints under the impact, and thence may be dragged unconscious to an all-night preacher. It is but another distraction from the old principle that there wasn't anything nicer than a good clean girl. The poor guy feels more and more that he is the victim of a conspiracy to snare him by artificial means, and he regards every dainty gloved hand as a boxer considers the fist of an opponent who has just smuggled six inches of lead pipe into his mittens.

Modern woman's suicidal rush to undress herself has helped her very little in the captivation contest. No man who orders a canapé cares much to be served with a full-course New England boiled dinner, and after the recent trend to nakedness, both summer and winter, there is little the dullest swain does not know of female construction, in the living meat. A guy can learn more about anatomy today, after a short stroll on the beach, than he used to know two weeks after the honeymoon quit. The latest bathing garb is composed roughly of two Band-Aids and a penwiper, with nothing but woman to hold them together. Wholesale nakedness is dumb of the dame, because she is cheapening her chief sales points, and is warning prospective prey as to what a horrible prospect the revealed body can be.

What you cannot understand is why so prideful a thing as a female can be so unwitting of her impact when romping on a beach or shorts-and-haltering around in the country. The same dame spends a fortune to prison herself in the hampers and harness we mentioned earlier, spends six hours on her hair and three on her face. Then she takes her guy to the beach and undoes all the good work by emerging nearly as natural as an egg. Then she wonders why the lovelight dies in his nasty little red eyes.

It will be a shame if that fragile wonder of nature, the woman, eventually puts herself out of business for what she was, and becomes a horrid amalgam of nothing much in particular. But she seems headed that way.

IV

I am basically a leg man, although I have been known to gaze upstairs with gratitude. And I am not going to let Mr. Christian Dior get away with it a moment longer. Mr. Dior has now almost destroyed womanhood with his latest ukase, which removes the knee and the elbow from women, in addition to the bust, which he has already dismissed as unworthy of notice.

I am weary of Mr. Dior. Twice a year he upsets the nervous system of the ladies, ruining their wardrobes and the dispositions, as well as bankrolls of their husbands.

He is the best public relations man in the world in his own behalf, for he has a semiannual way of choosing one particular spot in a woman's anatomy and making it unpopular. This always hits the front pages, suitable comment is made, and Ma rushes off to make herself modish again, and all according to a bald-headed Frenchman who sits on his big fat salon and giggles evilly at the mischief he is making.

The great man has now decreed the knee as the ugliest portion of a woman's anatomy, which is patently untrue, since the knee in my time has always been the demarcator of what you could legally see and what you weren't supposed to, and a mighty pretty dividing line, too, especially when dimpled. A sleekly clad knee, crossed negligently over another, is one of the most satisfactory sights in the world, as any fellow will tell you.

I am an elbow man, too, and a bosom man as well, and I will thank this Frenchman to quit sneering at all three vital segments of female assembly. At the rate he is going, he will do away with a few more things, such as legs and heads, and we will have nothing left but Mr. Dior's dresses, which lack appeal without stuffing. (The way he made them last summer, they lacked appeal even with stuffing.)

In my quiet, ill-tempered way, I intend to have a word with the fashion folk, next time I am in Paris. And I aim to set up an opposition camp, devoted exclusively to checkmating Mr. Dior. This will be easy, because I can invent a high-sounding fashion house and put out my own bulletins.

If Mr. Dior straps down chests, my house, which we will call Robert Le Salaud, will advocate practical nudity from the waist up. If Dior drops hems, Robert Le Salaud will lift them to ballet skirt briefness. If he outlaws knees, we will put costume jewelry on them and make them high style. The press is a powerful thing, and I hate to pervert it, but in this instance, as any harassed bill payer will tell you, a slight perversion is worthwhile.

It seems to me that there is no style that can make all women look well, and that this semiannual pandering to dissatisfaction has to stop somewhere, and Mr. Dior with it. And while we are on the subject of dissatisfaction in general, and the fashion folk in particular, let me draw attention to another piece of folly the girls have committed — I refer to the shift. There is no doubt that the shift is the most repulsive piece of drygoods that chicks have ever allowed themselves to be conned into. These shapeless shrouds might be useful to conceal advanced pregnancy or contraband. But they completely hide the salient points which make women appear different from men.

And the men are furious. They don't admire old bags. A campaign has started. And not a very subtle one. Several comptrollers of the family exchequers have flatly refused to allow so much as a buck to be spent on these jumped-up jellabas.

One gent I know, whose wife is a top-fashion executive, has a well-planned campaign to insult every member of his wife's clientele that he spots in a shroud. If he should happen to see them later in shorts or slacks he affects great amazement and says, "Thank the Lord, you haven't changed. I thought you were either pregnant or had gotten terribly fat." This is not making a hit with his old lady, who sells these fashion fads to the mentally impoverished American female.

Another gentleman I know, a rather testy type, has suggested legislation to make it illegal for a woman to appear in a sack unless her basic measurements, like 34-26-36, be painted boldly on her back, so that people will know what's inside the shroud. Another gent suggests that they wear buttons of political-convention dimension, stating, "Believe it or not, I'm a girl."

And that brings us once more to another point of contention. Pants. It's all right for those delectable girls in fiction to wear pants — not THE pants. But you gotta draw the line somewhere. Pants, I am sorely afraid, do not make the woman, nor does nudity enhance any more than the shift entrance. Very few ladies, generally buttressed by bras and girdles and the other accoutrements of femininity, can afford to go trousered into the harsh light of day.

Why they insert themselves in tight pants is one of the world's unfathomable enigmas. No bulge, no curve, no blemish goes unrevealed. A girl's got a mole? You just know the girl's got a mole.

But even so, a scar, a wen, a mole, is forgivable if the lady has the backside to fit a pair of pants. Main trouble is that 99 percent don't have the backside to fit a pair of pants. They have the backside to fit a dirndl, or some other forgiving garment that allows a broad to be broad without shrieking it to the world.

It is much as if one placed tight pants on rhinoceroses, elephants, giraffes, warthogs, whooping cranes, ground hogs, praying mantises, cobras, and hyenas, gave them all semi-human faces, and turned them loose in endless procession. You would think, really, that a lady who bathes occasionally would have some general idea of her personal geography, and would realize its limitations.

Beyond doubt's shadow, the Italians of all the races are the least admirably constructed for pants, except the Germans. The English are mostly what we used to call "single-butted" in North Carolina, being more straight up and down than out thataway, sideways, or from front to back. The slim Scandinavians seem best adapted; I suppose skiing does something to gear the rear to stretch pants.

If anybody cares a hoot about my britches, I can tell you one thing: they bag in the seat, and are roomy in the leg. At least I know what I look like in the privacy of my shower, and I would not like to inflict the image on the public.

Pants are one way for a girl to look ridiculous, but by no means the only way. I have had some occasion lately to hand several tight-skirted ladies into the low-slung cabs in New York and elsewhere, and have been confronted by an unusual situation. To a dame, the gals have requested that I precede them, and they tenderly close the door behind me while I slide painfully across the seat.

This is no reversal of old-time courtesy that bespeaks a fresh quality for the male, but rather a further indignation heaped upon the gentlemen, who now must shine his pants to a glitter in order to allow *madame* to climb into these swing-low, sweet chariots without showing a shocking amount of leg, or worse, splitting asunder a skirt into which she must now be inserted with a shoehorn.

We are past the stage where they sit down facing the street and carefully hoist the feet, and then snake-wiggle across no man's land. They have given up the battle, and I am working on a scheme where they will have to tip the doorman for his effort, as obviously a gentleman who enters first cannot search his pockets while sitting down with knees under chin.

I cry caution to the automobile boys if they persist in putting the modern auto underground, where a stepladder is needed to descend into its depths, because the ladies are not going to like ladders in their autos any more than they fancy ladders in their stockings. Either we retool Detroit or reform Paris, forthwith, because a lot of dew is brushing off the rose daily as the dominant male is goaded ever so gently into the vehicle with a sharp prod from behind from his fair lady.

The business of getting out of the car is even more fraught with contingency. Obviously, the swain cannot descend from the offside, for fear of being mown down by traffic, so once again he must either scramble across the lap of his beloved to hand her decently from the chariot — with eyes, of course, averted — or she is faced with wriggling out on her own and then extending a stevedore's helping hand to her escort.

I don't know how you fellas feel, but by the time I have been bulldozed all the way back across the seat, I reckon the least she might have done is pay the hacker and given him a tip uncommensurate with the usual female dime.

The cocktail-party stance has been changed considerably by the short, tight skirts. Used to be that a desirable female made for a convenient seat which would allow flocks of swains to surround her and ply her with — whatever they plied her with. Now she stands, just like one of the gents, because once she sits down she can't get up.

Somehow a guy doesn't feel as gallant about a lass who is bellying up to the bar as he feels about a maiden perched demurely on the corner of a divan with a bevy of young men nodding to her every beck.

V

It seems appropriate to insert a few words from the Old Man right here between the crossfire of random thoughts. The Old Man was a discerning fellow, comfortable and happy equally with pipe, rod, and gun. But not with the womenfolk. Now and again he'd toss off a pungent remark to indicate this, but always out of their hearing. Like, one day:

"Hello," the Old Man said. "What're you up to?"

"Nothin' very much," I said. "The womenfolk were cleaning house and it made me nervous."

"Makes me nervous too," he said.

The Old Man fetched up a gusty sigh and stuffed his pipe. "I reckon most folks would say we were just plain, cold-out, no-count lazy," he remarked. "It ain't necessarily so. Your grandma, if she ever saw fit to dirty her shoes on the waterfront, would take one look at the boys filling the benches and say something, with a sniff fore and aft of it, like: 'Look at those good-for-nothing loafers, so lazy that dead lice wouldn't drop off them, when they could be doing a hundred things we've been at them all winter to get done.' But, of course, that is women for you. It is the reason that, apart from having babies, no woman has ever done a first-class job of anything. They can't even cook as good as men. It's because they don't take the time to think. They're all like little old banty hens, scratching and pecking and looking around at every noise with a beady eye that's meant to be intelligent, but ain't."

I had to laugh a little at that one. If you ever saw bantam hens, you'll remember that they're never still, always peering at their backs, looking for lice with their heads swiveled all the way round, or pecking at their chests or under their wings, or scratching, or flapping wings, or jumping up on something, and always cackling, either with indignation, or in triumph when they've squeezed out another egg. Grandma — housecleaning, with a towel wrapped around her head, a dustcloth in one hand, and a feather duster in another — was just like a little-bitty old banty hen. She only paused to squawk.

"If you pinned me right down to it," the Old Man said, "I don't like nothing very much but a hot fire and a warm bed and a quiet woman to fetch me my food. I can generally manage the first two, but I been looking constantly for the basic ingredient of the third. Quiet, I mean."

Don't think the Old Man didn't work things out, though. He may have lost some battles, but he won the war. And he did it without any fuss.

As I remember, it was pushing on for Christmas when my grandma, Miss Lottie, pursed her mouth one day after she finished pouring coffee, and remarked that if there were any menfolk in the house worth the powder and shot to blow them to perdition they would bestir themselves and go find a couple of wild turkeys that were dumber than they were. "The price of meat," Miss Lottie said, "has gone up something terrible, and I do not propose to pay ten cents a pound for turkey. You either shoot it, or you don't eat it this year."

The Old Man cut his eyes at me over the coffee cup and allowed that he would finish his coffee on the piazza, because he wanted to smoke his pipe, and Miss Lottie had some definite ideas about smoking in the house. Unless she did it herself. She had the asthma and smoked Cubeb cigarettes for her chest troubles. I broke in on Cubebs at a very early age.

"The way of a man with a woman is hard," the Old Man said when he had settled down in his rocker and fired up the Prince Albert. "I reckon there's just nothing for us to do but leave her bed and board for a spell. It's a tough life, son, and you might as well recognize it early. Here we just got back from a hard week in the woods, up every morning before dawn, doing our own cooking, walking all day long, freezing on stumps waiting for deer to come by. My, my. Women are so unreasonable. If I had suggested even mildly that you and me ought to go turkey hunting, she would of found sixty different reasons to keep us home."

My idea of a woman, borrowed in part or whole from the Old Man, is one who has risen before dawn to feed the chickens, milk six cows, and slop the hogs. Then she comes in and washes and dresses a minimum of eight children, all hungry and at least three running temperatures of one sort or another.

Having shunted the children out into the snow to sell matches, to go to school, or practice arson — whatever it is children do — she should then wake the Lord and Master with a kiss and see that he is suitably stoked with ham, eggs, sausage — handstuffed, of course — kippers, kedgeree, and coffee.

After she bids him adieu, there are the beds to be made, of course, the house to be swept and the dishes to be washed, things aired and rugs beaten. Before she goes out to tend the garden — vegetables first, flowers second, because flowers are frivolous — she eats a stand-up lunch. This is because she is fighting against the time when she washes all the clothes, swabs down the bathroom, and does a tidy bit of sewing for the new little one who is about to arrive.

Then she must walk — not run, on account of the new little one — to the village to buy the necessary ingredients for the evening meal, unless she has been thoughtful enough to slaughter a pig or dress down a steer now ripening in the smokehouse.

And she really should give the bourbon barrel a kick to disturb the molecules, because the Lord and Master will be thirsty when he gets home and anything he hates is undisturbed molecules in his whiskey.

About that time of day we give her a rest, because we want her fresh for the kitchen. Naturally, she will serve the L and M first and dine herself off broken vittles.

There are few places left in the world where woman still has a proper respect for her mate. Africa is one of them, and it's the place for me despite the occasional hazards of the country, such as scorpions in the shoes and snakes in the bed, plus the added risk of encountering a love-maddened rhino on the way to the wash tent. The female of the human species still has no social status whatsoever, no political importance, and no rights before the local law. She is not called wife or debutante. *Manamouki,* or she-thing, is her name. Her only function is to breed extensively, minister to the comforts of man, and work eighteen hours a day in order that the master may loll about in comfort, drinking beer and soaking up the sun.

Here wives are not a luxury, or a form of madness, but a vital necessity. The more wives you have, the more beer, because each wife is responsible to provide the gruel-like mixture in vast quantities, at a hand's beck. The more wives, the more Kaffir corn, the more maize, the more work, the more kids. Kids, especially female kids, are important, because you can sell a fat young daughter for a nice price. Kids are social security.

I do not endorse the sale of humans, even in holy matrimony, although I understand it is not much different from the way we barter for brides with pretty presents and pensions to the in-laws. But I am enchanted with a place that still regards man as an important fellow, to be coddled and cared for so that he may improve his mind with leisure and prevent the poisons of fatigue from invading his frame.

In most tribes, if a man is fond of his wife, he makes her a present. The gift is long, thin leather straps cut from eland hide. She coos with delight, because these thongs will make it easier for her to carry the short ton of firewood she is expected to gather every day.

If a wife misbehaves her husband beats her up a little, and does not get hauled off to court to explain why. If he doesn't like her, if she's lazy and quarrelsome, he just kicks her out and tries to get his money back from her old man. If she persists in running away, her papa is morally responsible to refund at least a portion of the fee.

There is not too much complication in plural marriages. The girls generally have a hut of their own and a garden of their own. The husband calls around on each, separately, and attempts to divide his valuable time more or less equally.

It is not terribly expensive to surround yourself with wives and luxury. In hard times, a fat young maid is purchasable for as little as fifteen shillings. Even with momentary inflation, a healthy, hardworking woman can be acquired in Tanganyika for four or five pounds.

I tell you, Africa is strictly a man's country. I may set up shop there permanently, and if Mama is very good, I will buy her some of those carrying straps. She looks sort of silly lugging my trunk around on her head.

VI

The American woman is, by her own admission, the loveliest, smartest (chicwise), most intelligent, healthiest, richest, tallest, best-fed, best-housed, most worshiped, most pampered female on the face of the globe. God and

Good Housekeeping watch over her home. Santa Claus, Cupid, and the Easter Bunny are solidly in her corner.

According to her mood, she smells like date night in a harem or a breath of English spring. Nothing she owns ever fades, rips, or shrinks. Psychiatrists and agony columnists tell her how great she is. All our communications — newspapers, magazines, radio, television, giant movie screens in technicolor — fawn on her. Her marriages are made in heaven, and when the heavenly bliss exhausts itself, special designers come out of the woodwork to deck her in costumes calculated to snare a new candidate for ecstasy. Her sons become Presidents, and her daughters are all senators and spot-welders. She is never, never wrong, even when she *is* wrong.

Yet she is very possibly the unhappiest creature on the face of the globe, because she is undecided as to just what and where she is in the scheme. She is on the verge of destroying her basic commodity out of sheer envious ego. As she grasps the gavel and strides toward the rostrum her lacy handkerchief flutters unnoticed to the floor, and this makes her weep. She is on the way to becoming a definite third sex, having progressed too far to retreat, out of vanity, while simultaneously striving to preserve that which she had and is now in process of losing.

The American woman is finally trapped in a snare of her own devising, and you can read the box score of futility every morning on the third and fifth pages of the tabloids.

Let us dissect this frail creature, victim of her own intolerant ambition, but first let us establish that she has reversed her role.

Sometime back a suburban father eavesdropped a game of House, time-honored sport of the tots, in which his young son, a hearty, sturdy boy in the prime of childhood, was playing hard to get.

"Come on Jimmy," a little girl neighbor said. "I'll be the mama, you be the papa."

"No," said Jimmy, "I want to be the mama."

"But Jimmy," the little girl said, "mamas is girls. Papas is boys. I'm a girl and you're a boy."

"I don't care," Jimmy replied stoutly. "Mama is the boss in our house, and I want to be the boss or I won't play."

This particular father went away shaking his head, wondering to what state matrimony had come if even the children were cognizant of the change of status.

I never bought that old axiom about keeping 'em pregnant and barefoot in order to insure peace in the dovecot, and even came out, once, in favor of letting women eat at the same table with the menfolk. Time has proved me wrong. The initial mistake was made in treating women like people. We did them no favor when we allowed them the rights and privileges of the male while subjecting them to few of the penalties of masculinity. Crammed with propaganda and still giddy from political emancipation, Madame housewife has got entirely too big for her panty girdle.

Misplaced kindness to the female over the last few years has given woman time to think, which is tragic, because womankind has not yet learned to separate thought from intuition. She is the authority on the atom, the FEPC, the Communists, and the ECA. She knows everything, and ties her opinion to her own emotions, so that a momentary malaise will set her off on to a witch-hunt over the plight of the female Mohammed.

The American male is finding it increasingly difficult to be believably tender to a creature who knows everything and is little loath to admit it, in a high, shrill voice. He finds it difficult to pat the posterior of a mate who turns his parlor into a debating stand, and who is painfully insistent that she can do everything better than he can — or is mad and broody about the fact that she can't but won't admit it.

It is an unfortunate truth that the American woman continues to regard herself as a willowy sprite, subject to swoon, even though she may be six feet tall, with the muscles of a rassler and the appetite of a goat. One of the greatest ills of matrimony today is the lady's erroneous infatuation with herself as a faery queen, destined to dwell forever in a rosy fog of amorous foolishness.

Anyone who has ever lived with a dame knows women to be generally stronger than mules, with limitless endurance and nerves of wrought steel. Her demands on her husband are generally more economic than romantic, but she is so fattened on soap operas, romantic novels, and the cosmetic advertisements that she whimpers with dissatisfaction and brands her husband a lousy lover. She inflicts on her serf a stifling possessiveness that would soak the starch from Don Juan, but she still wants to live in bliss, with her stevedorish qualities unrecognized and her vestigial maidenhood enhanced by imposed delusion.

"Love me, you bum!" she shrieks, scourging him to the connubial cot with a whip. "Love me like Gable, or I will cut off your allowance. Love me, or I will quit work. Love me, or I will resign from Congress. I am smarter than you are and make more dough than you do and my friends are nicer than your friends, you seedy tramp, so kiss me sweet, or I will not let you go to the ball game Saturday."

Faced with this interpretation of love's young dream, Father sinks deeper and deeper into the hockey scores and the financial page. Finally, he seeks the company of something soft, fluffy, and brainless, and they ring up another divorce on the cash register of disenchantment. This leaves one more lonely dame with a fistful of Canasta cards, wondering what she did wrong and why that ungrateful beast had the unmitigated gall to spurn her charms for a moron who was also her physical inferior.

I submit it is getting tougher and tougher to fondle a female who is apt to be busy in the brain about her career, her clubs, her charity chores (fruit of boredom with what we used to call "woman's lot"), her involvements, and her ideological commitments. Speaking for me, if I make a pass at something, I am not reaching for the Heart Fund. I am reaching for a dame, with all the logical fixtures of same, except a runaway intellect that distracts her from the business at hand.

As the business of sex equality stands today, I see no reason why women should not pay alimony to men. Womankind in recent years has yowled like a tortured tomcat for equality of all sorts — businesswise, socialwise, and otherwise. But the second Mama starts slopping around the nest enough to drive Papa out into the night, she hollers poor-little-girl and immediately calls in a herd of lawyers to take the old man for his pants and shirt.

Perhaps if Papa is a naughty boy and deserves to get divorced, he owes Mum a decent living after he's rushed off with the redhead. But there is always the off-chance that what made Papa a naughty boy might be founded on the fact that he plain just didn't like Mama enough to hang around the lodge any longer.

In the matter of career ladies, I see no real reason why a divorced doll should get a cent from her husband. Certainly, again, she's entitled to half of what they built together, from furniture to the current bank account, but to punish him because maybe his grandpa had talent and rigged up a fortune seems wrong. And to take him for his future earning potential seems wronger.

If I ever got unhooked from my crown of thorns, I should endeavor to cut the books and the dogs and the piano down the middle, hack the bank account in two parts, and give the fugitive her choice of the furniture. I should also take an avuncular interest in her nonstarving future.

But if she hit me the big blow, I would do a very simple thing. I would run away, not do any work, and defy the lawyers to find me in Tahiti. The world might miss a lot of dubious literature, but the firm of Habeas, Corpus, and Lynchlaw would grow no richer.

The time-hallowed practice in divorce has been that on the sundering, the bereft bride takes the husband for his hat, cane, and overcoat, leaving him churchmousing around for the few remaining crumbs. This has largely come from the supposition that women are weak little chattels, pawns to the villainy of males, and once they have entered into the bonds they wish to sever should be allowed to walk off with the till — just because Pa's salted away a few bucks in it.

My personal warden has a small business. Why should she not keep me in high style after all these years that I've staggered into print? I'm tired, honey. I just don't want to work no more.

Kidding aside, the divorce laws are awful, archaic, and in the brave new world of outer space and the fresh fashions from Paris, the old girl rates no better than a dead heat, to be based entirely on need, not vengeance. The unsatisfactory wife has been eating free for years while Papa slaved. There is no need to guarantee her future if she can't earn her keep in the home.

Now that the girls are clamoring so vociferously for equal rights, lamenting their downtrodden status as second-class citizens, rigidly denying that the female is the weaker sex, I say let them have them.

I have conveyed my views to The Warden, and she, as usual, disagrees. She says that girls are too weak to work, although she has been chairman of my board since the day we refer to as Black Thursday in 1938, four thirty P.M., and the bride late, as usual. And she says that girls is so good and boys is so bad that when the household erupts, it's got to be the gentleman's fault, and he ought to pay for blighting the precious flower, for willfully planting rank weeds in the garden of domestic bliss.

Whereupon I say, look kid, when we bust up this crap game, I am going to sue you heavy for all the traffic will carry, and live me a life of ease on the Riviera or someplace, because I have put twenty years of hard labor in standing off that wolf and wrapping baby bunting in chinchilla, no lousy rabbit skins in this house, and I want some severance pay.

And she smiles sweetly and says: "Of course, bunny duck."

"But," sezzi, "where will you get the money to pension me off?"

"You," she says sweetly, and it seemed to end the matter. Write at the same address. I can't afford to leave home, no matter what the other husbands say.

A subtle poison spreads among women who have flunked the romance course through their own inability to decide who runs the roost. This is especially noticeable among the middle and upper-middle classes, and is most evident at the female get-together — the hen lunch, the Canasta party, the distaff cocktail fight. You may observe there, if you're my type of eavesdropper, the complete, clinical casualness of the rap against man.

His infidelities are retailed to all the eager hens. The worthlessness of men in general is stressed. Vivid details of his inadequacies in the mattress department are recounted with a lack of delicacy that would shock a commercial traveler. Seldom, except among the coarsest of males, would you hear such a caddish concert of carnal particulars as at a hen luncheon, with the girls' tongues loosened by the third Martini.

End product of this wholesale knock is that the gals who came in happy go away disturbed. Most women are gifted with total recall and an ability to color said recall according to their mood, so that the husband who comes happily home in the expectancy of a decent meal and a little peace suddenly finds himself set upon by a harridan with hooked fingernails, angered anew at an old and minor transgression that may have been a mutual joke for months or years.

Discontent is the seed which has flowered into the present schism between boy and girl. This discontent was watered and tended by the arm-wavers and the experts, the psychiatrists, authors, and agitators who discovered a ripe field for exploitation among the females. Our women are in the analysis stage now — no action is good enough to stand on its own as natural and uncontrived. The unnecessary second-guessing about sex has turned it from a thing of simple enjoyment into a clinical horror of deep-rooted complexes and overexpectation and self-questioning and clinical apparatus, until the process of climbing into the hay with a lady love resembles a tryst less than an experiment in biochemistry. The agony columns themselves, cluttered with half-baked psychiatric advice by unfrocked chiropractors, are enough to wreck the soundest liaison in the world if taken seriously. The scores of women's magazines have made everything from menstruation to eyebrow-plucking such a vast and complicated machination, in a big-business sense, and have showered so much expert advice on the female, that she now regards herself as a laboratory of mingled emotion and intricate machinery.

The books that are written by lady authors with definable moustaches and flat bustlines are generally contrived to set up a reaction of self-question, to breed dissatisfaction with that old cliché — woman's lot. In nearly all I have read, the man becomes a sort of villain whose prime purpose is to wreak as much misery upon women in general as he can. This in itself is an evidence of the jealousy of unfulfilled females who were unable to muster up enough allure to snag a provider, and have been shouting sour grapes, clothed in pseudoscientific jargon, ever since. Only trouble is that a vast number of normally attractive women take an old maid's (male or female) rationalizations seriously, and begin to brood about the leanness of their lives. It is comparable to the spoken poison the disenchanted ex-wives drench their friends with at the tea parties and hen lunches.

Woman's lot, alongside man's, is about an even shake, but there has always been a repressed desire in most gals — until they find out how good they got it — to turn into a boy. This is maybe because the boy takes the active approach to the girls, while the girls — legend says — were supposed to sit by and be asked. This applies no longer, so now we have a picture of an awkward female who wants to take the masculine initiative while maintaining a maidenly coyness in her life with the opposite sex, and it just don't work. There is a deep-seated shyness in man, bred out of generations of folkway, that turns him out of the path of the aggressive woman. Man has one pride — masculinity. When you encroach on that pride you have lost a lover and gained a son. Women who discover themselves married to sons shortly find they are living on alimony or sharing a room with another girl friend who made the same mistake.

Pants are a terrific symbol in today's strife between the sexes. Science has shown that there is room for only one person in the same pair of pants. No seat is so voluminous, no legs are so wide, that they will contain a man and wife, a swain and his maid. Womankind, reaching avidly for Pappy's britches, is in process of achieving such a sweeping triumph that she can wear her new splendor in lonely grandeur.

If there is one thing an average (average to mean normal as we know normalcy from a standpoint of sex, economics, and personality) man cannot stand from a lass is competition on his own terrain. He will go for tantrums and tears, for a burned dinner and a sloppily kept home, for hysteria and hurled crockery, so long as the lady in question refrains from competition on what he feels is a masculine plane. Competition will curdle the sweetest romance, because competition is what the old boy gets all day long in the trade marts, and what he needs least when he takes off his work clothes and arrays himself in lover's lingerie. When a man pursues a maid, when a man marries a woman, he seeks many things, but competition is the last thing he wants to find beneath the frills. This is why so few minglings of top careers last as marriages except in lip service, or joke, form.

I would say, too, that man possesses a much more basic morality than modern woman, and is more easily shocked by breaches of same. With the "new" equality has come a flouting, by the females, of old concepts of copybook morality, and the cockbird finds himself shocked to the gizzard by the naked social unmorality of the emancipated dame who figures she can do *anything* better than he can.

The domination of man by woman in our time has been predicated on gentle deception on the part of the girls, and when they quit leading us down the path, we are prone to buck and shy and finally to bolt. The new woman, unless she watches her step, is going to find herself emancipated right out of business. She has sacrificed femininity for masculine vanity in fields outside her accepted orbit.

Mind you, if I may make an exception, it seems to me the Government is being downright fusty in not kicking off an immediate program to send the ladies into space. There will be no peace in the house until we have sped a lady astronaut into orbit, and there is really no reasonable argument against shooting one — permanently, if need be — to the moon.

Women are generally tougher than men — weigh less, eat less, consume less oxygen, and are regarded as more resistant to noise, radiation, monotony, pain, loneliness, heat, cold, and heart disease.

There is no doubt that woman, not man, is the superperson of today. Husbands die like flies, but wives live on and on. Something in the chemistry of the female seems peculiarly adapted to the freneticism of modern living, if the incidence of widows traveling abroad on the old man's insurance money provides any yardstick.

Man rides jets and falls flat with an angina; Ma buys a new hairdo and appears ten years younger.

There is a slight complication about women's invasion of space at the moment — the fact that space drivers are supposed to be both jet test pilots and engineers. This, to me, is hairsplitting. Most of the women with whom I have driven in automobiles would make admirable test pilots of anything, since each sally-forth is a fresh adventure. As for engineering, anything a woman can't fix with a hairpin is unfixable by a corps of engineers.

I have been intimately associated with women since the moment I was conceived, and I have yet to meet one who was not man's superior in any specialized field, with the possible exception of fatherhood. She beats this oversight on her Creator's part by having a copyright on motherhood, the suasive gift of easy tears, and a choice of paternity via artificial insemination. Man has not yet been able to find an artificial mother for his children.

It is inevitable, when space excursions become commonplace, that woman will eventually dominate the outer areas, as she has generally managed to dominate everything she has touched since Eve went into the orchard trade. Space suits eventually will be the exclusive property of the fashion boys, and celestial advertising will be beamed straight down the old lady's neckline.

Woman's domination of the moon's interior (she has long used its exterior for the deadly bemusement of mankind) being a stark certainty, I see no reason why milady shouldn't serve at least a rough apprenticeship before she takes over the going concern. Let her suffer the early stages so she can brag later about how rough it was before Rodriguez dipped the neckline on the space suit.

As children have a deplorable habit of being untidily born in unlikely places, such as taxicabs and airports, we shall have to face up to the first astral childbirth, and get it behind us.

There are passport difficulties to be overcome here, and we might as well whip up a planning committee now. The first mother to be delivered of issue en route to Venus or some other such way-stop is going to cast a permanent shadow over all the other mothers since Eve, and I would prefer her to be American rather than Russian.

So I say strike the shackles from our women and cut them loose in space. If only to free them from the Martini lunch and encourage them, after the novelty has worn off, to return to the kitchen!

VII

But if you think the American male is suffering, look what happened to the Japanese gent after centuries of acting like an Oriental Simon Legree in meting out treatment to his women. No matter which way you view it, Pearl Harbor was a disaster. But did you ever think of it from this angle?

The American G.I. visited the most terrible vengeance on the Japanese that was ever imposed on a vanquished race. I refer to the emancipation of the Japanese woman, into whose tiny hands since the war came the vote plus equal privilege in social and economic life.

This is no momentary revenge, but a permanent punishment which will be passed on from father to son, so that Tojo's great-great-grandchildren will curse their ancestor as the wrecker of male supremacy in Japan.

As long as there is a Jap alive, Pearl Harbor will be remembered and mourned. Surely, if the warlords had foreseen the consequences, mass hara-kiri would have been ordered on December 7, 1941, and the Emperor's reign of Showa, or peace, would have continued.

The Japs, when they climbed down out of the trees and started snubbing the hairy Ainus who still swung from the branches, immediately began a campaign to keep women in the kitchen and out of public life.

They worked hard, for centuries, to get their womenfolk

in hand, and finally succeeded. As is fitting in a civilized country, the wife deferred to the husband, and man was king in the house. He also was king outside the home, because Mama confined herself to her domestic duties, and let the old man wear the commercial kimono.

When Father came home from a hard day at the geisha house, with worries of the rice crop and the pickled-radish shortage heavy on his neck, he got comfort. He didn't run into a lot of deep conversation about politics and the atom bomb.

He never came home from the office, expecting dinner, to find a note saying that Mrs. Okimoto was off on a speaking tour, stumping for Congress. She didn't let the babies holler while she played golf or wrote historical novels. She was not encouraged to march in demonstrations, picket the Diet, appear on radio quiz shows, or racket around the country fomenting discontent among the other housewives.

The Japanese man was very happy for many years by ruling that women should neither speak, read, write, nor think, and discouraging any overtures in these directions by administering a sound rebuke with a stick.

In America today, about the only fields in which man remains dominant are cooking and designing clothes, two womanly functions which have been temporarily discarded in Mama's mad race to be a senator, a movie star, or a Wall Street executive. It is not unlikely that in a few years the Jap dolls will be invading the privacy of man's social bathhouse. There will be reverse-English geisha joints with a flock of slick-haired male entertainers to lure the old lady away from the rice paddies and the washpots.

They will insist on choosing the old man's kimonos, and

every Christmas he will get a mess of horrible ties from female relatives. They will be telling him to lay off the saki and to cut out the cigarettes. They will tell him how to run his business, and push him out of politics.

The male will start living out of a can and washing his own dishes, while his wife, via Radio Tokyo, gives out handy hints on housekeeping for men and belabors his ears with soap operas called "Nishimoto's Other Wife," meaning the happy little moron he was espoused to befo' de wah.

Ah, yes, truly we wreaked a great and lasting vengeance on the Japanese male, and it serves him right for chucking his weight around. When his wife tells everybody blandly: "Ah so, Fuji makes the major decisions, and I make the minor, but only I determine which is major and which minor" — when he hears this, let him remember Pearl Harbor and curse the Greater East Asia Co-Prosperity Sphere.

The silly Son of Heaven didn't know when he was well off.

In any war, even with women, just before the cease-fire, there comes a moment when you find something, maybe only one teensy little thing, in the enemy to sympathize with. This tetch of fellow feeling was inspired by the tremendous amount of wordage which has been expended on discrimination in restaurants and drugstores and cafeterias. Far be it from me to expound on the social conscience of our times, but I do wish to pitch in about discrimination in another area.

This is guaranteed to make me several million friends of any color, creed, profession — but only of one sex.

It's the problem of unescorted women drinking in bars. The color question has been pursued for about as long as the string will stretch, and there has been a vigorous movement for equal pay for women, according to ability.

In the general clatter, it appears to me that nobody has lit on a vital miscarriage of justice in our time — the untenable place of unescorted womanhood in our saloons.

It merely has to do with stopping at a bar for a casual slap of hooch, after the work's done and the lady wants a little liquid inspiration to get her home to the fresh set of problems of being a spinster — or, indeed, a worthy matron with shopper's arches.

In most states where whiskey is sold to standers-up, a gent can nip into a bar for a nip, nip off and be on his way. But this is not so with the fairest flower of our race. And girls, I have found to my expensive sorrow, get just as thirsty as boys.

Even if there is no law against the serving of solitary females in bars, there is very definitely a strong set against it. The lorn lass who stops off to have her psyche half-soled before she goes home to rinse her unmentionables is regarded coldly as a combination of crying lush and prostitute before she takes the first sip of a small beer.

Even in New York City, a village of great elasticity, most bars regard the unattached woman with the same distaste a cabdriver has for a man who carries a suitcase with an umbrella strapped to it.

At very worst, she is told to go hustle someplace else. She is often told that women can only be served seated at a table. If she rides along with this gag, the first fourteen fellows at the bar try to send over a drink.

The general theory among the older breed of saloonkeepers is that women are nothing but trouble — loud, weepy drunks, pickers-up of men, and, at the very best view, poor spenders.

This may be true, but we have given them the vote, they are supposed to be getting equal pay, and if they can't grab a fast snort against the miseries, what sort of bloody democracy are we running?

I have never liked the hearty, loud, and generally dull atmosphere of any stag bar. I like to drink with dames. Men's clubs bore me. Not that I hang out in sleazy saloons trying to pick up stenographers, but a fair face and a pretty leg enliven any boozing den.

With me all the way in this attitude were the late Tim and Joe Costello of the revered bar and grill on Third Avenue. They made their female clients more welcome than the men, and took stringent care that there would be no monkey business with a lonely lady who just couldn't face the subway without a bit of bolster.

I was — well, let's say a friend of mine was viewing a comely damsel with a glint in his eye one night in Costello's, and Tim leaned over the counter and said, in his best Irish: "Here, now, me bye, there'll be no neck-archin' in moi saloon."

My friend averted his eyes fast. Tim kept an impressive array of shillelaghs behind that bar.

PART TWO

The Girls
Who Make
Life Beautiful

As you know, I'm a sullen cuss of the old school when it comes to the weaker sex. In fact, I've spent most of my working life griping in public about the girls. Not only is it good copy, but it's what they deserve. Furthermore, they need someone to keep them honest.

At the same time, I wouldn't want it thought by my faithful followers that I'm above giving credit where it's due. So, every once in a great while when I come across that rare specimen of womanhood who has heard and attended to the message as purveyed by yours truly (or maybe even come to it natural-like), I want to tell the world.

There are eight such lovely ladies who follow hereafter,

and one oddity that I'll get to in a minute. I guess the only thing they have in common is the fact that at one time or another I fell for them. The range goes all the way from the Queen of England, through a substitute stripteaser in New Orleans, to a weary old lady in Spain.

About that oddity, now. The Old Warrior, otherwise my better half, makes an unscheduled appearance at the end of this section. I'm not making any excuses, mind you, but she said it was only fair, and I just couldn't seem to persuade her different.

Piaf

Not since Joan of Arc's untimely end has a nation mourned more a departed lady, which is remarkable when you consider she was born in the street, reared in a house of prostitution, had an illegitimate baby when she was fifteen, was as ugly as sin, went unsteady with the wrong fellows, and was named Sparrow, with reason. Piaf probably created more Gallic sympathy by her passing than Lafayette ever managed on an unscheduled ocean voyage to America.

Nobody ever had as much luck of the bad sort as Edith Piaf. She *was* born accidentally in the street. She *was* raised by her grandmother after her mother deserted her at the age of two months. It was a respectable *maison;* Granny employed twenty girls.

Edith *did* have the woods colt at fifteen, and the child died of meningitis. Edith owned a less functional liver than nearly anybody for the last double decade. She fell in love with a prizefighter named Marcel Cerdan, and he copped it in a plane crash. She had a thing about younger men, which caused her pain, and she looked like a butcher's assistant in her little black frock.

And, she was lovely.

She sang "La Vie en Rose" — which made her famous — and everybody who ever heard her, saw the sad eyes, and watched the wonderful hands, immediately fell sadly in love with whoever was closest.

She was incomparable in a way that Toulouse-Lautrec, the degenerate dwarf, was incomparable in his own field of art. She was incomparable as Maurice Utrillo, an illegitimate drunkard, was incomparable in his painted feelings for Paris.

She was just plain incomparable.

She had eyes like great wounds and a mouth like a huge sob. Her hands were testimony to torture, and lacked only crucifixion scars to make them complete. She didn't have a body worth watching, but out of her mouth there flowed a soul.

It was the kind of voice that ennobled the listener, and you did not pause to consider that she was named Sparrow because she was a homeless waif of the Paris streets.

You did not consider anything. You merely felt that life was pain and then came death and in the meanwhile, with luck, there might be love.

Piaf quit this sphere much too early for the world's health. The Bible says that no sparrow's death goes unnoticed by God Almighty. I hope He's on the ball with Edith. She could certainly qualify for the special place for the folks who die wounded by life, and she is bound to improve the heavenly choir.

Queen Elizabeth II

She once undertook a six months' circling of the globe to assure her loyal but distant subjects that things were going well with her and to give them a look at the first sovereign ever to visit some of their lands.

Never was a more staggering junket attempted. The Queen and Prince Philip covered nearly 50,000 miles and visited fourteen countries. They traveled by train, plane, ship, helicopter, jeep, auto, and horse carriage. The complete program for the royal tour filled a closely written book an inch thick. A year went into the scheduling of the trip; even the Queen's walking time from ship to shore and from aircraft to auto was figured on a time sheet.

The tour involved a piece of logistics roughly comparable to a small war. The royal luggage weighed twelve tons, and Army, Navy, and Air forces were deployed in supporting roles. The Queen had with her a royal household of ten people, including two ladies-in-waiting, with military officers of various ranks dancing in perpetual attendance. But they were still living out of the suitcases, and they hardly ever settled down long enough to get the laundry done.

Elizabeth and Philip attended 185 state functions, balls, parties, luncheons, and dinners. They planted trees, unveiled memorials, laid wreaths, held investitures, broadcast speeches, opened parliaments. With each function they performed in a free parade.

By way of diversion — diversion! — Her Majesty and consort displayed a seemly interest in sheepshearing, cricket, woodchopping, horse racing. They attended plays, ballets, a music festival, and twenty-seven displays by children. On the royal agenda were a couple of Australian mines, a steel mill, a *haka* dance in New Zealand where she was symbolically attacked by a Maori warrior and then given a ceremonial club with which to defend herself. In Tonga she sat cross-legged on the ground with the mountainous Queen Salote while eating roast pig with her fingers.

The Queen shook about fifty thousand hands, changed costumes an average of four times a day, and reviewed countless troops and constabularies. Through it all she never missed a serious engagement or fell ill. Despite crowds that gave you an outdoor claustrophobia just to watch them crush each other, she hit all schedules smack on the button.

Elizabeth's sense of perfection is as good as that of any star actress. She spent hours on a special face makeup. In Sydney the lighting system for a big ceremonial dinner clashed with her makeup, her costume, and the seating arrangement. The Queen, checking the house, ordered the system changed. Learning that winds are high in February and March in parts of Australia, she had the hems of her shorter shirts weighted so that no vagrant breeze might flirt with the royal knees.

Her wardrobe, which included more than sixty special costumes with shoes and hats, plus two hundred pairs of white gloves, never presented her as anything but immaculate. Perhaps the makeup helped, but she never looked drawn or tired. She is a model of long training in studied public deportment. Her walk is superb, her carriage magnificent, and as a result of dieting she is as slim as a wand. Probably the word "radiant," used in every newspaper account, has never taken a heavier beating. It is a natural radiance. But I do know that the Queen is never unconscious of her appearance.

One day a handsome Australian aide, Lieutenant Commander Michael Parker, was helping her into a limousine with a Plexiglass dome, which keeps off the nonselective rain and still allows the throngs to see Her Majesty. She turned to Parker to say:

"Michael, how do I look?"

"You look like an orchid under cellophane, Your Majesty," Parker replied, and the Queen beamed like a maiden.

Millions thronged to see her. Never in my life have I observed such an emotional impact of an individual on masses of people, or such a solidification of mass loyalty for commonweal. Crowds came in from the country and slept in the parks. They ate box lunches and stood in baking heat, in the rain — not for hours, but for days.

They redecorated their homes and bought new outfits. They spent fortunes to dress their cities in bunting and arches and extravagant lighting effects. Sydney alone spent more than five million dollars to decorate the streets, and shot off fifteen *tons* of rockets on the evening of the Queen's arrival. Melbourne probably spent more, out of sheer civic jealousy. The humblest home in Australia was hung with flags.

By her stunning performance Elizabeth refuted those Socialist critics who had said royalty was getting too expensive, and wasn't worth the million and a half dollars it cost annually.

As an American I should like to say: "God save their gracious Queen! She is needed by this world."

Simone Signoret

The trouble with Madame Montand, which is Simone's square name in French, is that she is married to a man who is younger and bigger than me. The trouble with me is that I am married to a woman who is younger and bigger than me. Where my new romance will end nobody knows.

I deplore the habit of my new fiancées having their husbands to lunch because, after all, you have to be polite to the gent, as he is grabbing the check, and one does not, ever, bite the feeding hand.

Madame Montand, whom I shall marry, like I said, is not the prettiest girl I ever saw. But when you look at her you think she is the prettiest girl you ever saw.

There are not many actresses around these days, and La Signoret has started a new trend. She can act. She does not sell bosoms or a plump rear end or a classy chassis. She has slightly baggy eyes and, to be charitable, she ain't as far away from the you-know-what age as she is close to it. She has the odd wrinkle or so and nothing much to offer in the way of a

figure as a marquee attraction. The hair is reasonable non-
descript, and she has a way of squinting her eyes that does
them less than justice.

I wonder if it's really wrong to be engaged, without tacit
permission, to another man's wife, when your own wife
doesn't know about it either.

Lena Horne

A slim, lovely lady with a square yard of handkerchief in her hand stepped out. She was dressed in something
big-ruffly which caught and complemented the golden lights
from a tawny skin. She flicked the handkerchief, and then
she flicked lashes over black eyes as big as saucers, and then
she flicked a dimple large enough to secrete a walnut.

The three-piece background group throbbed behind her,
and she began to sing in a furrily intimate voice with odd
gasps and strange halts and breath suspensions in it.

La Horne's voice reached out and clung to the people in
the crowded nightclub. It traveled from falsetto to bass. It
hopped and skipped and jumped and crawled slow and easy.
Like honey that is too cold to spread. It got sly and humorous and just a little low down, and now and again it sounded
like the crinkle of freshly starched sheets and the sound of a
light snapping off. It sounded as comforting as a hot water
bottle on cold feet, and as soothing as a lullaby, and as
frankly inviting as a tossed head and a deliberate wink. She
finished one song in a solid hush, and away back in the

boondocks one man's voice said reverently: "Jesus Christ. . . ."

Whenever Lena sings the crowd is hushed. And wherever Lena sings, there is a crowd.

Although Lena may possess one of the most beautiful faces in public, she is not opulently endowed with a figure which might detract from her vocal delivery. She generally wears very bouffant frocks — what she calls "girl clothes" — with lots of tulle and flounce and flutter, but which make nothing of her figure as an asset. She does not flatly sing suggestive stuff, and makes no obvious pass at a male audience. She does rather direct her mood at women, who seem to be allied with her in a general insinuation that true love is harder on girls than it is on boys.

Lena knows what she is doing to the people out front, but very possibly does not know, technically, how. She cannot read a note of music. She was complaining, once, about a piano player who kept missing the point of pianistic augmentation of her voice. "The trouble with that cat," said Miss Horne plaintively, "is he knows too much music. He reads it, but he can't feel it. Too busy with sharps and those tired old flats."

What suits Horne is whatever she feels surely is the right way for it to be. Lena is a passionate rehearser, and if she had her way she'd have her accompanists working for an hour or so every afternoon, trimming what she calls "slop" out of a phrase here, adding a lilt there. Watching a rehearsal is a tremendous experience in an inexact science.

Horne will show up in a sweater and slacks. She has a soft, slurred, almost incredulous voice — her normal speaking tone, as if she herself did not believe what she was saying.

"We got a kinda old musical cliché goin' in that thing we we're tryin' to do last night. It oughta go oodle-ee-ahh-Huh! right there in the third part, you know where I mean, where I say 'that voodoo, that you do,' and Joe, now you got to do a little something with the tomtoms or something so it'll go oodle-ee-ahh-ahhh-Ha!, a little brisker, more, because we ain't playin' a wake here those people spendin' good money so let's us try it now, say?"

No onlooker is ever quite sure what happens to the intimate plumbing of a piece, but after a few minutes all the oodle-ee-ahh-ahhhs are tucked into the arrangement the right way, and Miss Horne goes satisfiedly off to the one Martini she permits herself before she works.

There has been no necessity to mention to now that Lena Horne is a Negro who has found no undue cause to exploit her race as an adjunct to her art, any more than Joe Louis needed to be a Negro in the ring. Lena is a very light tawny gold in color, about the same color white women seek to achieve in Florida. She has a flock of freckles on a thin nose, a great big dimple, and wavy black hair with a few lines of gray penciled through it. She has enormous eyes. In appearance she could easily be a member of any of the Mediterranean nationalities.

"Back when I was a kid coming up," she was musing one day, "somebody told me I was too light to make a success out of being a Negro. Said maybe I ought to be a Cuban or a Brazilian or something. As a matter of fact my great-great-grandma was a stewardess on a ship out of Martinique. I hope she was a real voodoo, although I am sure it could have embarrassed my grandmother to have a voodoo in the background.

((80))

"Tell the truth, I feel mostly like an American — which ain't odd, considering that's what I am."

Stormy's Mother

Everyone knows I'm a shy fellow given to blushing at the sight of a well-turned instep. But I did get myself sidetracked on a street called Bourbon, Bourbon Street being the spiritual and physical home of the striptease, which has been scourged from less sinful cities than this.

As anyone who's ever been there knows, and even those who ain't, stripteasers are not exactly a rarity in New Orleans. For every salt worth his sea legs they're part of life and liberty. It's seldom, though, that any one of 'em stirs up the mother image.

Ordinarily I would say that the flexible part of peeling has been overwritten, but I think I have come up with what used to be known as a scoop. I have just encountered mother love of such high-octane potency that Mama is now shedding her garments as a substitute for Daughter — Daughter having fled to matrimony and pregnancy as an antidote to fame.

"Ah just can't get used to undressin' in front of people," says Ma, whose name is Josephine Spellman, and whose daughter Stormy is possibly the most famed stripper ever to bare a goose pimple on a street where naked ladies come eight to the bar. "Took three people to run me up on the stage when the time come to undress."

Stormy's mother is billed as "Stormy's Mother." That is

explanation enough, because Stormy is the doll who became nationally famous when the entire campus of Louisiana State University conspired to throw her in the university lake. People came from far and wide to see Stormy, a disdainful-looking lallapalooza who sneered at the customers. When Stormy hung up her G-string, to marry a chitchat columnist and tackle motherhood, a great gap was left in New Orleans' elite nightlife.

But Mother, although she had been a demure cashier up to that time, leaped bravely into the breach. It seemed a charitable deed to give the clamoring customers Stormy's Mama, if Stormy herself was unavailable.

Stormy's Mama comes from Atlanta, Georgia, and she is very decorous.

"Ah never bump frontways," Stormy's Mama modestly tells me. "Ah always bump sideways."

A bump, for the uninitiate, is a kind of convulsion in which the midsection is hurled sharply at the audience, to the accompaniment of strident thumping of a drum. It is the climax of a truly dramatic performance. A sideways bump would involve a sudden shifting of hips, as in an impassioned rumba, and would be defined as refined.

Stormy's Mama never divests herself of what the trade calls the teaser.

"The teaser," she says, "is the fringe or whatever. Under the teaser comes the nets. You can see through the nets, but not quite. Ah never get down to the nets. Ah always keep on the teaser."

Stormy's Mama is forty, she says, and her daughter is twenty-three. They marry early in the South. Stormy's Mama has a nice shape, very much like Daughter's, and the same sort of haughty face. Her soft drawl comes oddly from a shapely contoured starkly coiffured head.

"This is still very new to a girl who never believed in taking off clothes in public," she says. "Whenever Ah recognize anybody in the audience Ah can't hardly stand it."

"But," she says, with an air of desperation, "Ah've gone so far now Ah can't quit until Ah make *Life* magazine. Then Ah aim to re-tire."

Stormy, it might be said, once commanded a big spread in *Life,* apart from vast coverage by the national press. Like daughter, like mother.

"Ah guess Ah'm kinda old-fashioned," she says wistfully. "But I declare to gracious Ah don't think Ah was cut out for this kind of work."

Margaret Mitchell

She never knew a lot of long, tough words, but her dialogue was ear perfect. Her descriptive stuff was as sound as any the tonier professionals have ever produced. Her research was both colossal and accurate. The critics sure knocked her around, but about the only real fault you could find with *GWTW* was that it was so easy to read that eight million people read it.

One of the things I always admired about Miss Mitchell was her complete lack of professional authorship. She spent ten years or so hammering out the single epic she knew so well, and was content to float on the splash it created and the money it made. She never made a move to rush into print again with a shoddy substitute, which would automatically have sold several million copies on the impact of her name. She sat quietly at home in Atlanta, counted her money, looked after her foreign rights, and never chucked her weight around a nickel's worth.

You cannot set common critical standards against a book that so inflamed the public imagination that the citizens of thirty foreign lands are familiar with the burning of Atlanta and the strains of postwar reconstruction. *GWTW* was the top literary phenomenon of the age, and as such strode strongly away from the miserable stuff that in the past and since has been labeled "historical novel."

Old Lady of Spain

I don't know why she keeps creeping back into my mind, but I would like to try to tell about her, anyhow. I've never been able to get rid of the memory of her.

She was a very, very old lady, with her chin under her nose, and a skin the color of leather. Her hair was white, and so were the old-woman's whiskers on her chin. She had no immediate family but lived with distant relatives, and so was possibly a nuisance.

She came every day and sat at the corner of a road in Palamós, near which I was building a little white house. There was a garden in back, always full of things growing.

There was a wall around the house, with flowers on the wall, and the Mediterranean blue in front.

The house was a cheerful house, and it shone in the warm sun. It was a busy house, too, workmen singing as they made a clatter, gardeners always planting things. Although the house wasn't finished, friends had already started to come, and especially a lot of young friends.

They kept the record player going eighteen hours a day, with the volume on full, and they were always racing around the yard in shorts — young, handsome, sunburned, and noisy kids, full of the innocent devil and of themselves. They necked casually in the yard, and capered like puppies.

The old lady sat in her rusty black weeds and nodded in the sun, and smiled secretly to herself, possibly remembering a day when her legs were long and strong, and she first got kissed in a garden, and then got engaged, and then got married, and then had her children. She watched them grow up and go away and then she buried her husband and later her children, one by one, living on and on until she had shrunken to a wisp of flesh; a woman no more, only a burden and a trial.

She needed care, and the house of her relatives was a poor one, so that there possibly was not enough space or food for an old woman who was of no earthly use, and who would not die. So it was decided to send her to a home for the aged, where there were facilities for worn-out old people like the old lady who sat at the corner of my garden and listened to the carpenters sing and the kids playing Sinatra and Crosby records on the machine.

So she came another day, and I waved, as usual, when I

drove off to the village, and she nodded and smiled through her toothless gums, as the sun breathed a little more life into her cold old bones. She was trudging home when I got back, bent nearly double, walking uncertainly as the very old walk, wide-legged and splayfooted. She did not look up as I passed.

The next day there was a commotion, and the police had come to my garden. The sun was warm and the breeze was brisk, and some of the late flowers were still in bloom. The carpenters were wrangling and the record machine was playing one of Joe Bushkin's piano recordings, and there was a great bustle in the house.

The police were taking something tenderly down from a fir tree, a tiny black bundle. The old lady had come to die in the last place she loved. She had tied a scarf around her neck and sunk gently to her knees, her hands clasped in prayer, and when she reached her knees the scarf jerked taut on the branch to which she had tied the other end.

I was proud that the old lady had come to die in my garden, for one last look at the new, bright thing she loved, while the record player blared and the carpenters clamored. In a way it was a compliment to us.

Tallulah

The Southern Belle who makes all other southern belles sound like a tinkle, was once deeply enmeshed in a tearing-down, million dollar fight with Benton and Bowles,

Proctor and Gamble, some sort of shampoo called Prell, radio jingle writers, *Time* & *Life* magazines, lawyers, letter-writers, other people — and hamlets — with the same name, and a new water system on her farm which cost thirteen thousand dollars. The system not the farm.

I went to call on my old neighbor at the time, carrying a fifth of calf's-foot jelly and a sympathetic look. I said hello, baby, they're treating you rough. Tallulah took over from there.

"Darling," she said, "darling, you can't know what I've been through with that bloody water system costing thirteen thousand dollars and taxes like they are and Gaylord is moulting from the strain Gaylord is the lovebird who is sitting on your neck and the reason I've got only one is the damn birds won't talk if you've got two they just sit and drool over each other and I haven't been able to sleep a wink I'm so upset and confused over the whole awful thing my God today I called room service and when they asked me what I wanted I told them a bourbon sauté and I couldn't be in my right mind you know very well because I love you that I never endorsed a bloody thing in my life not even an opium pipe which reminds me of the story about Jeanne Eagels and Fanny Brice Jeanne was on the fire because she'd endorsed some sort of cigarette or other and everybody was being very artiste about it and pulling faces at her and Fanny asked somebody how much poor dear Jeanne got for the endorsement and they said five thousand dollars and Fanny said My God for five thousand clams I would endorse an opium pipe and darling you know yourself I never even so much as endorsed a reefer and I wouldn't have ordered a bourbon sauté if I'd had a matinee on today because you know how I feel about my work and just ask me all the questions you have in mind but ask them loud because I'm so nervous I'm a wreck and it isn't a publicity gag at all it's a kind of pride I have in my work you know darling when you lived next door and I was saddled with that stinker *The Eagle Has Two Heads* you know I always turned up cold sober for every stinking performance and now look at me I've come down with my spring leprosy and I'm just a wreck and it's all because of this awful Prell thing the man wrote a singing commercial with my name in it to sell some vile hair oil or something and you remember that it was Beaverbrook who once said only three people in the British Empire were automatic front page news — George Bernard Shaw, Tallulah, and the Prince of Wales — and you know very well that when somebody says Tallulah nobody ever answers "Tallulah Who?" and I never slept a wink last night because darling this is serious with me and my privacy has been invaded and you know I don't need the money it's a point of principle I've got my name to think of and I've got a million letters here to prove that I don't need a last name mentioned to have my privacy invaded and I intend to fight them to my last ditch Gaylord come down off that dash-dash mirror poor darling he's frightfully upset and who can blame him so am I and now ask me a question, darling."

I do my own interpreting when I talk to Tallulah, and the gist is still that she thinks no commercial product has the right to use her name without permission, since she is the only Tallulah around who is immediately identifiable by her first name. Stealing Tallulah's purse has always been a theft of trash, because of an uncontrollable generosity, but she has invested her years in her unusual first name, which she had from her grandmother. I think it was real unchivalrous of the hair-soap people to use it without her permission, and now if she will just take Gaylord off my neck I will say that maybe I have proved a point in her favor because I never mentioned her last name at all.

(Despite a certain amount of clamor from some heretofore-unknown possessors of this rare monicker, Tallulah had the last word and the offending commercial came off the air.)

Virginia

Women are so unpredictable. I don't know what came over the Old Warrior the day she went berserk. I've always gone along with that "better to be abused than ignored" bit, especially applied to her. But she came lurching into my study holding a fistful of clippings, and she was madder than a wet hen. She said she wasn't going to stand for it, and when I said stand for what, she said the way I always made her come out in print like a monster.

"People are surprised when they meet me that I haven't got two heads," she said.

"That's strange," I replied. "Somehow I always think of you as having two heads. And you're a natural-born heavy, like my friend the late Louis Wolheim, or Jack Palance."

"But the way you write, people don't know whether I'm blonde or brunette, fat or slim, tall or short."

"Neither do I, half the time," sezzi. "Sometimes you're

blonde, sometimes you're brunette, sometimes you're striped. A lot of the time you're fat until you decide to put me on a diet — and then you get skinny. The only invariable thing in your makeup is your disposition, which is invariably awful."

So she went on to say that Earl Wilson called his helpmeet the Beautiful Wife, and that Freddy Othman called his gal the Bride, and that Bob Considine had a kind word to say for Millie, and that Lennie Lyons was always plugging Sylvia, and Hal Boyle seemed to like to write about his wife by name and pedigree.

"Nobody even knows what my first name is," she wailed. "What have I got to do, write a column myself or go on television to rate a plug in your column?"

"Look, chum," I said. "You are exactly one year younger than me, to the day and hour, and I know how old I am. We have been spliced for years, and I have had to fight for ownership of my pants every single day. I may be a husband, but I sure ain't no press agent. You catch me getting coy in print about my home life and they can turn this battered old Underwood into hair curlers, because I am through.

"The only true satisfaction I get out of writing this thing," I said, "apart from money, is that I always figure to win any battles I have with you for public consumption, for Lord knows I never won any in real life."

Then I went on to tell her that she was a prop, a stock villain, and she was Mama in my mind and the Old Warrior as well, and I wasn't going to disillusion any male readers and lose the source of my best dull-day copy. Then I beat her a little bit, and gave her simulated skunk coat to the Salvation Army.

But now and again — well, once anyway — a man's resolve breaks down and he has to hand out the kudos where it's deserved. You see, I was blessed with a talented interior decorator for a wife. To her goes the gold star with oak leaf for the fact that people tell us our house in Spain is one of the loveliest in terms of taste, that they have ever seen. God knows how Ginny managed it when one tiger takes up a whole wall in the living room and two Cape buffalo lower over the fireplace in the office; a leopard is draped springing-fashion over the lady's bed, and some say that alone would induce nightmares. It could have been a zoological garden, but this robbers' cave turned out to be the kind of joint flossy magazines take pictures of.

On any terms, it is a good man's house, with big fireplaces and lots of space for books — an enormous desk to hold my clutter, and plenty of room to turn around in.

But the snapper is that we get more *oohs* and *ahs* out of the women than we collect grunts of approval from the menfolk, although the bar is functional and there are plenty of soft places to set. The reason I say this is practically revolutionary in the decoration business is that the entire house is done as an African farmhouse, on a helter-skelter basis, and is built entirely around game trophies!

What is even more amazing, the joint has been visited by four internationally famous male interior decorators, all of whom expressed approval that was *not* spurious, and even went so far as to pinch an idea or two for their own use.

And one was the gent who redecorated the White House,

and more or less seriously suggested that the only solution for Mrs. Virginia Ruark, when she asked him what to do about Papa's trophies, was "Get a divorce."

We have twenty years logged in the holy bonds. I take all the credit for this miraculous longevity of stir-time with the same dame for just one reason. I have been a hunter since I was six, and since I have been married I have generally tried to preserve the better specimens of the chase. Gentlemen, I tell you, a man who can fill his home with the dessiccated carcasses of animals and birds — when his wife is an interior decorator — is a man of extreme talent, or maybe dumb luck. Most of the talent lies in first presenting a challenge, and then in saying: "Yes, *dear*."

But the challenge is the thing. The average dame spends her life trying to make the chintz come out even with the easy chair. Women being generally conceited, when you heave a fish, a deer head, and a stuffed ruffed grouse at her and say: "Make this into a thing of beauty, *madame*," it is possible that she will draw on her feminine reserve and complete the commission. All you have to do, really, is put her on her mettle.

Having been raised rurally, I seem to have spent most of my early years stumbling over the moth-bit black bear rug, with the open jaws that forever claimed your ankle on a dark evening. There was the fox head over the mantel, the stuffed owl and the pair of quail under the glass dome in the dining room, and the panel of dispirited ducks. A mournful deer peered at a lugubrious elk, and the general mood was that of Sunday in a cemetery.

This is what starts the fights in a house: "One perfectly

good room ruined by that musty old moose, that moth-eaten whitetail, that moulty old pheasant, all jumbled together to louse up *my* beautiful home. Who wants to look at a fish, even if it is the record, every morning in the breakfast nook?"

And this, fellows, is where we get sneaky. A good fish, surrounded by the right colors of paper and decoration, can *make* her breakfast room, if you just let her think she thought it up all by her little old pink-dimpled self. . . .

We have to use African and Indian trophies to illustrate my point, because that's all I've got handy here in Spain. But the same can be said of any noble game, be it a bobcat or a turkey-feather fan. It's where you put it — or rather, where *she* puts it — that makes all the difference between more money for taxidermy or alimony.

"Mama," sezzi, "you claim a good decorator can do anything with the materials at hand. Why don't you make me a house where the trophies'll be high style, *très* chic, instead of being just a bunch of old dead things hung on a wall? I bet you could if you tried. You could plant philodendron in the elephant's feet, and . . ."

When you say philodendron to an interior decorator, you got him hooked. Philodendron is a plant that lives well inside, and it is dangerous to leave anything with a cavity in it lying around loose, because the next thing you know there'll be a philodendron in it. I once knew a decorator who tried to plant one in a sore tooth.

Mama accepted the challenge. We built a kind of fun house, styled somewhere between California and Cataluña, with overtones of Africa and Fifth Avenue, and when it was built, of plaster and beams and fieldstone, the head-hanging started.

Naturally, like any other small boy, I wanted to put everything I had, right down to the warthog, in a jumbled mess. Now, a domestic trophy room is awful enough, but an international big-game trophy collection would make Noah scuttle his ark. Generally speaking, the walls are crowded with Rocky Mountain goats and wildebeests, and lions and leopards, and buffalo and antelope, and the tusks of elephant surround the fireplace, and on each side is a zebra divan, and cougars mingle with Indian sambhurs. The bar is zebra-striped and the coffee table is rhino hide or elephants' ears, and all the cigarette boxes are zebra. There is an elk next to a panel of impala, and when you get past the Alaskan brown bear pelt on the floor, and the head of the Asian ox, the gaur, mingling with a whitetail deer, and some rugged ideas of what constitute colorful pictures, you don't need the dik-dik mounted whole to make the whole thing a Madame Tussaud's cocktail party, especially if the rhino is placed right next the sailfish you caught in Acapulco.

"The first thing," Mama said, "is that a lot of this junk has to go. That oryx makes me want to cry every time I look at him. That gaur looks more like a cow than a gaur. We got plenty of livestock without him. But his hide's lovely. It'll do for a rug. And do you really *want* an eland when you've got a rhino, two Cape buffalo, and an Indian water buffalo in the same room?"

"It's a big room," I said. "It's forty by thirty by nineteen feet high."

"Yes," she said, "and it's got a desk as big as a garage in it, and two divans and two coffee tables and another desk and a drawing table, and we got to have someplace to put the elephant's tusks you're so proud of. And what about the elephant's feet?"

"All right," I said. "Go ahead and get busy with your philodendron."

She got busy all right. She turned what I consider a reasonably fine bunch of trophies into a decorative effort that has been squeezing the plaudits out of visitors ever since, and I didn't mind the fact at all that the little *casita* where we keep summer furniture, the lawn mower, and the firewood had a few extra heads and hides in it. Such as the rhino, the oryx, the gaur, and the Indian water buffalo. *And* the eland.

The old lady balanced the delicate against the massive, each complementing the other. She took the best tiger and stretched him upside down over the fireplace in the living room, so that his chin was on the mantel and his tail touched the ceiling. The tiger rates a gasp every time a stranger walks through the door.

She gave the mangiest lion to the undeserving poor, and stuck the handsome redheaded *simba* over the fireplace in a little upstairs sitting room. And then broke her solemn vows by framing the fireplace with the second-best tusks, and it came out fine. In both instances there were no other animals in the room to compete. A good tiger or lion doesn't need any competition.

The biggest elephant tusks sat together by the office fireplace, back by the elephant's feet, which, sure enough, she had planted with philodendron.

In the study, she rigged two Grant gazelles and an impala in a sliding musical upward scale on one wall, the two big buff claimed another wall, and all they had to look at was a Masai shield and some of my own primitive artwork, plus a rather stylish sable antelope who had come to replace a vulcanized rhino. At the other end of the room, two more delicate heads — a waterbuck and an Indian cheetal deer — looked all the way across the room at the two Grants and the impala. You caught their importance because there wasn't any close competition.

She managed to fill the room with eight heads without overcrowding it, and it is a room so large it would have held thirty heads in the classic tradition of culture.

She went real high-arty in her own bedroom with my best leopard, mounting him diagonally on the white brick wall over her bed head, with one paw flapping languorously over the rough gold-cloth headboard. The room has nothing much in it but white walls, a black rug, and some black-and-gold Catalan furniture, but it jumps out and bites you.

She went sissy on me in my bedroom, and everybody said it was her best effort. She grouped two Thomson's gazelles around a long-necked gerenuk, a close cousin, against a gray-green background, and the gold animals against the green take you all the way back to the African plains.

Mama claims that just scattering zebras around helter-skelter is bad decorating, and will louse up any scheme, so she took most of my hides, had the heads and legs trimmed, sewed the squares together in a wall-to-wall carpet, and the guest bedroom is a sight to see.

This hide business, by the way, can make a very satisfactory adjunct to the decoration of a house. Ordinary deer or antelope hides, sewed together, make lovely rugs and bedspread throws. In South Africa, they make a fantastically beautiful thing they call a *kaross,* or throw, out of silver jackal or wildcat hides. The same can be done in America with fox hides, wolf hides, even coyote or wildcat hides, and I should imagine a lynx *kaross* would be astonishingly lovely. For small skins, sewed together to make a piece of rug or bedspread, skunk, or fox squirrel, or even the little gray or cat squirrels can be powerful pretty if flung carelessly in the right direction.

There was a new room stuck onto the house lately, and the old girl suggested firmly that what was needed was a really decent greater kudu with a fine lesser kudu for counterpoint. She practically scourged me off to Africa, and as I was leaving, spake in a strong, wifely voice:

"If you can manage to make it down to Tabora in the rains," she said, "there's one hole in the wall that can use a good sable — now we've taken down the rhino."

"Yes, ma'am," I said, which is the whole trick in the business of having the house the way *you* want it, and staying married.

PART THREE

Maman Toddy and the Child Grenadine

At a time when the romantic, historical novel was outselling all others, Ruark wrote his first fiction.

It was a romantic, historical spoof. Its heroine was bustier, its men lustier, its episodes more shocking and its revenge sweeter than in any book of that time.

He set it in the South. But it was a South that his imagination — not his southern background — presented to the reader.

Grenadine Etching, his first novel, introduced his first fictitious heroine. Here is the story of her growing up in the care of an old-fashioned Mammy (New Orleans style) whose

*devotion and teaching fostered the most fantastic belle ever
to emerge from the pages of a book.*

Grenadine Etching started from scratch. Her
mother, her father, her infant brother, all were dead on the
day of her birth. Her home had burned down; Dr. O'Gorman, who delivered her, had been found in a ditch with a
bullet in his brain. Nobody cared much — life was cheap in
New Orleans. No one cared, either, that Maman Toddy, a
giant Negro witch, was raising the young white child in her
little house on Rampart Street. People did not pry around
the domicile of Maman Toddy. She was feared by the blacks,
and the whites accorded her a great respect.

Maman Toddy was no quack, no clumsy mutterer of in-
cantations, no amateur pointer of bones. Born on a slave
ship of savage parents, she was bought at auction, together
with her mother, by Pierre de Chandelier, a wealthy planter
whose great plantation, Désir d'Argent, was a showplace in a
locality of showplaces.

Toddy lived as a house servant on the plantation of M. de
Chandelier until her fifteenth year. At that age she was a
sight to see. Seven feet six inches tall, she weighed a slim two
hundred and twenty pounds. Her black skin shone with
health, and her teeth were cubes of sugar in her red mouth.
Her features were as cleanly cut as those of an Assyrian princess. Her pear-shaped breasts pointed sharply upward, and
her legs, long as those of a thoroughbred race horse, carried
her proudly about the plantation.

She fell under the eye of M. de Chandelier, who was then

fifty-seven years and nine months old, according to the family Bible. *Le grand seigneur* was a bachelor from choice. He was an evil old man, and half the woods colts of the country could call him pappy. His nose was long, and burst on the end with a network of whiskey-bred ruptured veins. A thin moustache fell over the corners of his wet red mouth, the lower lip of which drooped like rubber. His eyes, pouched and bloodshot, were as yellow and evil as those of an old goat. His hands were clammy, skinny, and webbed with purple veins. A distended belly gave his skinny legs the appearance of wind straws, and he smelled bad. Pierre de Chandelier weighed a slight one hundred and twenty-five pounds with his pockets full of silver dollars, and was altogether as unsavory as a toad.

He made *une passe,* or unwelcome advance, at Toddy one day in the woods, where she had been sent to gather scrapple for a Yankee visitor from Philadelphia. The scrapple trees were in full bloom, and Toddy had little difficulty in filling her apron with this succulent bivalve. Unwilling to go back to the house as yet, she sprawled on the ground and gave herself up to a voluptuous enjoyment of the hot, moist spring day. The lush black earth was cool under her back, and she wore only a thin cotton frock. Birds sang in the dogwood trees, frogs croaked by the bayou, and the breeze toyed in the gray-bearded cypresses, running its fingers through the Spanish moss as a lover ruffles the curls of his adored. It was a nice day.

De Chandelier watched her from a thicket. When her eyes closed he advanced on cat feet. He stooped beside the drowsing girl and kissed her quickly on the lips. *"Ah, mon bonbon de chocolat,"* he whispered hoarsely, *"comme tu es belle aujourd'hui."* He reached for her with hooked hands, and the young girl leaped to her feet.

"Je suis belle, peut-être," she snarled, *"mais pas pour vous, m'sieu!"* As de Chandelier stepped back, aghast at this insolence, Toddy attempted to brush past him. He reached for her again, and she knocked him flat with a backhanded sweep of her left fist.

That night, as the slave girl slept on a king-sized pallet athwart the door of Mlle. de Chandelier, Pierre's maiden aunt, she was roughly roused by the grasp of strong hands upon her limbs. Toddy was powerful as ancient bourbon, but her lithe young strength beat unavailingly against the muscles of the ten field hands who seized her. She screamed and struggled, but a young girl, even one who stands seven feet six inches tall, has little chance against ten laborers who average seven feet eight inches among them.

"Take the bitch to the yard," said de Chandelier, blowing smoke from a thin cheroot. "Take her to the punishment pen."

The punishment pen, a quarter mile distant from the big house and shielded on four sides by a twenty-foot hedge, was fully equipped with instruments to teach tractability to slaves. There was a set of stocks, several whipping posts slimed with blood, and an upright coffin called a hotbox, where disobedient slaves were left to ponder their wrongdoing. After five days the box was tipped over into a lime-filled trench, and the time and expense of building a new coffin was saved. There was a Spanish Inquisition-type rack, on which slaves who stole were stretched. There was a forge, a bellows, and a branding iron marked LS/MFT, which stood for "Lowly Slave/Made Foolish Trouble." There were iron boots for crushing feet, and copies of the *Congressional Record,* which were read in the local patois to the more serious offenders.

"Stake her out," said de Chandelier, dismounting from his favorite stallion, Homme de Guerre. "Stake her to the four saplings and hand me my whip."

Picking up a steel-tipped blacksnake whip, de Chandelier beat her until his arm ached and her long, lovely body was a web of crosshatched bloody pain. Casting aside the whip, he lit another cigar and muttered, *"Alors,* fetch me the branding iron with my special *insigne."*

White-hot and sputtering, the iron was brought to him by the slave in charge of branding recalcitrant slaves with M. de Chandelier's special *insigne.* The slave bowed low as he handed the iron to his master.

Holding it finickingly in his gloved hand, de Chandelier sought out a spot untouched by whip and pressed the iron to her shoulder. Toddy's body went rigid, and a gasp passed her lips. A smell of seared flesh mingled with the night's odor of peach blossom, wayward skunk, and jasmine. There, on her slim black shoulder, were two livid letters, angrily red: "UW" — "Unreasonable Woman," the sign of the damned, the special *insigne* of the House of Chandelier. Toddy fainted.

"Leave us," M. de Chandelier said, and the slaves faded into the night.

"This," said de Chandelier, tossing away his cigar, "is what happens to my property when it sees fit to disobey me. I am master here, my raw black beauty, and I do not think you will rebuff me again. When you have healed sufficiently I will see you once more."

He called his horse, which called back to him, and they cantered away. Toddy regained consciousness three days later, and feeling more than a trifle sore, went calling on Maman Obeah, who lived in the woods.

Maman Obeah was a witch. She could, by pressing her gray-pink palms to an aching spot, rid a patient of pain. She could bring a straying lover into line. She could cause an enemy's hair to fall out and his eyeballs to pop. She could cause prosperity, bellyache, and babies merely by muttering the correct appeal to her gods. She was one hundred and three years old, blind, dirty, and unhappy, but she was one with infinity, attuned to the heavens, and the mistress of all mortals. Her only companions were a tame wildcat, a talking owl, two castrated male rabbits, and a three-legged jackal. They lived in the house with her and added to its aroma.

"Di' moi, ma tante," said Toddy, dragging her aching body into the rude lean-to in which Maman Obeah lived with her pets, and gagging at the stench, *"di' moi,* how can I avenge this insult? Teach me the laws of the night and the swamps, the language of the birds and beasts, and make me forever an acolyte of Papa Chango. I am the nineteenth daughter of the nineteenth daughter of the nineteenth daughter, and all my male progenitors in Somaliland were witch doctors and psychiatrists. Tell me, O Queen of the Night, how can I get hunks with this landed toad, my master?"

Maman Obeah reached for a cup of hellbroth, compounded of steamed scorpions, and took a long, satisfying swallow.

"If you are serious, my daughter," she answered, "if you

are willing, if you will give your life to the task — if you will give yourself into my hands — I have a scheme which will start by complete vengeance against your master. And less than one hundred years from now the white man will curse the day he brought us to these shores."

"I am willing," Toddy said. "Tell me what to do."

"For a start you take the white of an egg. . . ." And thus began the girl's initiation into black voodoo.

Two weeks later her lashed body was completely healed. No scars remained, with the exception of the livid "UW" on her shoulder. "Wear it," Maman Obeah said, "as a badge of shame and pride, ever to remind you of what we must do to the white man. Wear it in good health."

Toddy wore it — and in later years she had the scar set in pigeon-blood rubies carefully grafted into the skin.

Four weeks later Toddy appeared before her master. She looked languorously at him over her shoulder and smiled slowly.

"Good evenin', suh," she said. "Ah is hopin' you is in de best of health."

De Chandelier's eyes lit up, after he struck a large sulphur match that he carried for that purpose.

"You're as pretty as a picture," he said. "Where are you going?"

"Ah'm goin' fo' a walk in de sun," Toddy said, flashing him another smile. "Down to'ads de scrapple grove."

"I feel a need for exercise. I think I shall accompany you — at a respectable distance in front, of course."

"Ob co'se," Toddy said.

It was dark in the scrapple grove — dark as night — lightened jewel-like by pricks of sun through the velvety leaves of the scrapple trees. The grass was green and soft as velvet, or at least baize, and reeked with four-leaf clovers.

"This is my lucky day," de Chandelier said. "And I can use some. Lost four hundred twenty-five thousand dollars at dice last night with that young scoundrel, Butler. *Ah, comme tu es belle, chérie.*"

"*Ah, oui, c'est tout pour vous, mon maître,*" Toddy sighed, knowing that she would hate herself in the morning. And M. de Chandelier, his eyes feverishly bright, advanced toward her, his breath coming in gasps. . . .

The next day was Friday, the thirteenth. De Chandelier, inspecting his prize alligators from a safe perch on the corral fence, suddenly lost his balance and fell among the beasts. He was eaten slowly by the alligators, as a gourmet savors a luscious hors d'oeuvre. Afterward the alligators died of ptomaine poisoning.

Scarcely before de Chandelier's screams had subsided, Mlle. de Chandelier, feeding her pet pompanos, stumbled and fell. She landed in the feeding trough, and before her shouts for help could be heard she was nibbled to death by the pompanos. Mme. de Chandelier, Pierre's mother, was feeding her guppy fish at the brink of her mammoth pool when her foot slipped. While her sister-in-law, Mlle. de Chandelier, was being nibbled to death by pompanos, Madame was being nibbled to death by guppies.

Gran'mère de Chandelier, out in the pastures breaking in a new colt, was pitched from her sidesaddle and broke her neck instead of the colt.

Three sisters of Pierre — Adelaide, Melisande, and Hortense — died in childbirth within an hour of each other, to the intense amazement of the countryside, since not one of the trio was married.

Three low-flying storks committed suicide.

Antoine de Chandelier, an uncle, choked over his morning herring, and before the doctor arrived had breathed his last.

Gout got Dieudonne de Chandelier, another uncle.

Illegitimate Cousin Pierrepont de Chandelier was shot by an irate Cajun husband as he sought escape in the pirogue of the cuckolded muskrat trapper.

Seven thousand two hundred and twenty-nine slaves of assorted sexes escaped to Canada.

The great house, nine barns, a summer cottage, a hunting lodge, the slave quarters, the boathouses, a racing grandstand, three smokehouses, a corncrib, a tobacco barn, nine bourbon distilleries, and seven acres of fresh green mint burned to a cinder from no explicable cause.

In the statehouse Governor Honoré (Pass the Pralines, Mon Père) Pompier, a distant relative on the distaff side, was poisoned by his mistress.

In New Orleans a house of ill fame burned mysteriously, cremating all occupants, which included two ill-starred female cousins, banished from the House of Chandelier for refusing to wear crinolines, and four male cousins, visiting during Easter holidays from L'Université de la Louisiane. The university baseball team was beaten next day, 77-2, by L'Université de l'Alabam.

By six P.M. (Confederate Saving Time) on Saturday, the fourteenth, no vestige — human, chattel, or physical part — of the great family of de Chandelier remained alive. Even the safe deposits, including hoards of bullion, silk stockings,

deep-frozen steaks, and priceless butter, disappeared, because the Bank of the Brethren of the Absinthe Frappé
burned to the ground, crisping a defaulting teller who was
working overtime to cover his defalcations. It was later
proved by a genealogist that this luckless fellow, named
Rappaport, had been intimate with a third cousin of Pierre
de Chandelier.

Deep in the swamps, in a smoky hutch, Maman Obeah
turned from petting her talking owl, her tame wildcat, her
altered rabbits, and her gimpy jackal, and smiled through
toothless gums at the young Toddy.

"*Tu fais bien, ma fille,*" she mumbled.

"Ah tried hahd," Toddy said, still filled with shame. "Ah
give the whole dynasty a run fo' its money."

Word of the fate of the de Chandeliers spread swiftly
through the countryside. It became known among the masters of the plantations that Toddy was the only surviving
relict of the once-great family, and a delicate problem was
posed. Since all the de Chandeliers were dead, with the exception of an outcast fifth cousin who had fled to Vermont to
be a painter at the age of fourteen and whose name was
never mentioned, there was nobody to claim Toddy. It became known, too, that Toddy had spent much time with
Maman Obeah and that M. Pierre once had had her flogged.
The *seigneurs* of the area began to put *deux* and *deux* together and came up with a resounding *quatre*. Still, the
huge and vibrant Toddy was a nice dish, and hitched to a
plow, could do the work of twenty mules. The wives of the
seigneurs, however, having no desire to be eaten by their pet
Pekingese and/or Pomeranian, cast aside feminine timidity
and had their say.

"You bring that great monster within ten miles of Sans Pensant," said Mme. Amélie Boudreau to M. Anatole Marie Jean le Baptiste Boudreau, "and I take away your thirty-seven concubines. Thirty-seven little girls I don't mind," continued Mme. Boudreau with Gallic practicality, "but seven feet six inches of sorceress I draw the line at. *Pardieu! Les hommes!*"

Mme. Symphonie de Livaudais was brief.

"Bring her here," she said, "to my beautiful Mal de Tête, and I will give her no chance to work her witchcraft on you, *petit pois*. I will take my sewing scissors and cut your throat myself. *Écoutez-moi, mon ange?*"

"*Mais oui*," said M. Hercule Antoinette de Livaudais. "*Mais oui, et oui encore, p'tite lapine.*"

And so through a devious period of indecision, litigation, and civil war, Toddy was adjudged, by the Supreme Court of the State of Louisiana, to be a free agent. Nobody desired to buy her, even for a song, and songs were free in Louisiana.

The upshot of it was that Toddy moved to town. After working for five years in the bordello of Mme. Shoofly Ramirez, where she commanded a certain novelty value along with a one-legged Iranian girl and an albino, she had scraped up enough coin to buy a small house in Rampart Street. She brought Maman Obeah into town to live with her. When Maman Obeah died, from an overdose of scorpion broth, at the age of one hundred and nineteen, Toddy inherited all her lore, including the two eunuched rabbits, the talking owl, the crippled jackal, and the tame wildcat. The tame wildcat had become wild, the talking owl was misanthropically silent, the rabbits suffered from obesity, and the jackal had lost the use of another leg, so Toddy mercifully killed them all with a club and buried them with Maman Obeah. She collected a new set of household gods and went into business as a licensed witch, a *bruja*, a *mama-loi*, a practitioner of voodoo.

Maman Toddy, as she was now called, set a stiff price for her services. She considered herself a scientist, and so she was.

When Grenadine was old enough to talk, her first word was "man." This was unusual, since she had not seen one since the day of her birth. After the death of Dr. O'Gorman, who was ceremoniously planted in a night-blooming cereus bed by Maman Toddy (and after that the flowers never bloomed again), the huge witch went out of business. She banished her assistants, took down her shingle, and went about the chore of raising the white child according to her notion.

Grenadine was oddly reared. Maman Toddy never gave her milk, for one thing. For the first month she fed the baby on broths of her own brewing. After that Grenadine ate meat, at first carefully minced. By the time the child had discovered her third tooth she was gnawing on a pork chop and smearing her little face happily with candied sweet potatoes.

She was a healthy child. She never cried. She never had colic. After her third month she never wet herself again. She walked at six months, said her first word at seven. "Man," she said gravely, around the corner of a pork chop. "Nice man."

She loved Maman Toddy with her whole soul. She would sit contentedly for hours in a sling hung to the black woman's shoulders. *Maman* crooned to her as she worked at her various chores—sweeping the house, cooking the simple meal, manufacturing juju powders, preparing wax figurines, which were labeled with the names of prospective victims and which lay neatly in cotton-filled cases. *Maman* sang songs of Africa, songs of Cuba, songs of Martinique, songs of New Orleans. She knew them all.

By the time Grenadine was a year old she could croon right along with her mammy. Toddy took the contralto, and the baby took the lead in a thin, sweet soprano. By the time she was two she was singing contralto and Maman Toddy had reverted to mezzo-soprano. Grenadine's favorite songs were "Shortnin' Bread" and "Babalu," a song of the slaves who worked the cane fields in the Oriente Province of Cuba. At two *Maman* presented her with a small pair of *bongo* drums, a dried gourd filled with buckshot, called a *maraca,* and the jawbone of an ass, which, when stroked, made melodious rhythm. Painstakingly the black woman taught her how to play them in a manner to invoke the demons of the swamplands.

At three Grenadine got her first pet, a tiny gorilla, which Maman Toddy had ordered, by jungle grapevine, across the broad ocean, via Casablanca, Dakar, and finally Leopoldville. It came back by way of Capetown, Durban, Bombay, Colombo, Perth, Sydney, Funafuti, Oahu, San Francisco, Panama, and Gulfport, Mississippi. It was quite hungry when Toddy took it from the ship after a slight altercation with the mother gorilla, who stood three feet shorter than Toddy and, as a consequence, lost.

Grenadine was entranced by the gorilla, whom she promptly named Brandy. Brandy was a little smaller than Grenadine and, for a gorilla, was quite blond. It was impossible to tell whether Brandy was a little boy gorilla or a little girl gorilla, but they played happily together for a' that. They slept in each other's arms, shared each other's food, and never fought except when Brandy indulged in his/her one peculiarity, which was eating little songbirds.

Generally Grenadine won the fight, since her baby teeth were longer and stronger than Brandy's, and by the time Brandy was two his/her quick little gorilla's mind was able to associate a punch in the mouth with mockingbirds, and by virtue of the conditioned reflex, he/she ceased masticating any and all creatures with feathers. Until the day he/she died Brandy was puzzled when Toddy killed and picked a chicken for the pot, or cut one's throat just to keep her hand in the black-magic business.

When Grenadine was four, *Maman* let her out of the yard for the first time. She sent her to market; the French Market, that is, where one can buy sweetened coffee redolent with chicory, jambalaya, red beans, and nearly anything else in the way of food that the heart desires.

They made quite a pair as they strode off to the market, Brandy walking a decorous two steps behind his/her mistress, as the custom of the time demanded. For laughs Maman Toddy had tied a scarlet tignon over the gorilla's head and a ruffled white apron around his/her middle. He/she carried a small flat basket and a fly whisk. Grenadine's long silver hair was braided in three heavy plaits, two of which fell down her back, and the other upswept to hold a heavy dew-fresh rose. Her eyes sparkled, the intermingled green and brown catching the morning sun, until they looked like cat's-eyes, the polished shells sailors brought back to barter for beer and other things. The child was dressed simply in a parody of a grown-up's frock, her miniature bustle jouncing saucily as she walked barefoot along the street. One thick hammered gold bracelet ringed her wrist; one thick hammered gold earring hung nearly to her shoulders. New Orleans caught its breath, released it, and caught it again.

Nothing much happened in the French Market. Grenadine bought the things *Maman* had told her to buy—eggs, lettuce, chives, oranges, bananas, shrimps, pecans, peppers, avocados — and as she selected each choice she passed it backward over her shoulder to Brandy, who put it in the basket. She counted her change correctly and passed on to the next booth. When morning shoppers attempted to question the little girl, Brandy snarled so fiercely that they backed away, intimidated. Grenadine smiled sweetly and said nothing beyond a courteous *"Merci, m'sieu,"* or *"B'jou', madame."*

Only one mishap marred the morning. A well-fed French poodle, escaped momentarily from its mistress, ran up to Brandy, ruffled and growling. Brandy broke its neck with one munch. Poodles, although strange to behold when clipped after the fashion of a hedge, wore no feathers, and hence, to Brandy's ape mind, were fair game.

After that the crowd made a lane for the little girl and her pet, and Grenadine, humming *"Auprès de Ma Blonde"* under her breath, walked sedately back to Toddy's cottage.

When Grenadine was five, Maman Toddy began to instruct her in sorcery. The child was a willing pupil, because Toddy made a sort of game out of the lessons. They would sit in the yard sometimes for hours, while the black woman put the little girl through her catechism.

Toddy would say, "Tell me, what is a *ouanga*, honey?"

"A *ouanga*," Grenadine would answer, "is a kinda little dummy. You stick pins in it."

"How does you make one, honey?"

"Well, you take some beeswax, and you make a little man or a little woman."

"What else does you put in it?"

"You put some fingernail clippin's and some hair and maybe you tie a piece of cloth on it."

"Where does the cloth come from?"

"It comes from the clo'es that the person you want to hoodoo wears."

"Where does you leave a *ouanga* when you wants to witch a person?"

"You leave it in the path leadin' from the house where the person lives, or you put it under the pillow of the person, or you let it go into the dining room under a plate the person is gonna eat outa."

"What happens when you hoodoo a pusson by fixin' a *ouanga* and leavin' it in the right place?"

"That depends," the child would say gravely.

"How you mean, that depen's?"

"Well, maybe I might want to make a person go away. I put some go-away powder in the fire when I'm meltin' the wax, but I don't stick any pins in the *ouanga* when I got it done. I don't put any curse on the person — I just catch one white dove and kill it and let the blood drip on the *ouanga,* and then I think powerful hard about where I want the person to go. Then I say some words — you'll have to tell me again, Mammy, I always forget — and by and by the person goes away."

"You didn't tell me where you put the *ouanga!*"

"Under his pillow, of course, so's he'll never rest easy there no more."

"That's good, baby. Now tell me, s'pose you wants to kill a man?"

"That's different. You catch a little goat and cut his throat and let the blood drip on the *ouanga.* Then, when the moon changes, you take a black rooster and cut his throat and let the blood drip on the wax. Then you take some fingernails and a little hair from the person you don't like, and you sprinkle 'em into the wax while it's meltin' over a fire made outa bitter ash and green toadstools and weasels' livers."

"Uh, uh, what then?"

"You get a young brown girl and take off her clo'es and make her lay down on the floor while Scipio beats the *bongos.* Then you go into a trance and you pray quiet to yourself, and when you come to the brown gal is foamin' at the mouth. You wipe off the foam and smear it on the *ouanga* and send Scipio and the brown gal home."

"Tell me mo'."

"Then you take a rattlesnake and split it wide open and put the little wax dummy inside and sew it up again. Then you feed a baby rabbit to the rattlesnake."

((*115*))

"And?"

"The rattlesnake gets sick and throws up the figure on Friday, the thirteenth, when the moon is green, and you are ready to go to work. You take the figure and you hide it under the plate of the person you want to kill, and when he lifts up his plate and sees that little thing, all stuck full of pins, he knows he ain't for long."

"You didn't tell me about the pins," Maman Toddy would chide. "You didn't say a mumblin' word about them pins."

"The pins," Grenadine said, "have been dipped in toad's gall and steamed over a slow fire made out of owl's feathers and rabbit's feet. Then you heat 'em white-hot in a fire made from cypress moss and lightwood knots, and when they're about to melt you stick them in the *ouanga.*"

"Where do the pins come from?"

"They come from the clo'es of somebody the person you want to kill has done something bad to."

"What happens after the pusson you wants to kill sees the *ouanga?*"

"His hair drops out and his meat turns sour in his stomach. He can't sleep at night. His wife runs around with other men, and his house burns down. His eyes get red and his fingernails drop off. Somebody steals his money, and his daughter has a two-headed baby. His horse gets the botts, and cholera gets into his pigs. His chickens get the pip, and it rains and drowns his turkeys. He's cold when it's hot, and he's hot when it's cold."

"Is that all?"

"No, ma'am. The meat plumb drops off his bones, until

bymeby he jest lays down and dies. When they find him next morning his eyes are staring and his mouth wide open. A black cross is burnt into his brow, and the little *ouanga* has melted away."

"What melts it away?"

"The closer the man comes to dying, the more the little figure melts. When finally he dies dead, the figure has melted away and gone back inside him. His soul flies away on rabbit's feet and owl wings, and he burns in hell forever."

"That's fine, baby. Here's a piece of candy your *maman* done made just for you."

"Are you sure it hasn't got any hemlock in it?" Grenadine would ask darkly.

"Shame on you fo' doubtin' yo' mammy," Toddy would say, smacking her bottom. "Is they any questions you would like to ask?"

"Well, one," Grenadine would reply. "Why do you spend so much time and take so much trouble? Seems to me it would be simpler to take a gun and shoot whoever you were mad at."

"Honey, you don't understand. Doin' it my way don' leave no nasty questions for the coroner to ask, like why has this genman got a hole in his haid, and why is his th'oat cut from ear to ear? Voodoo is so much neater than them other homicides — unless, of course, you got a nice neat wisteria bed to bury the corpus delectable under."

"I understand," Grenadine would say. "Can I go play with my horned toads now, Mammy?"

"Why, suttinly, honey, suttinly." Toddy would laugh in

her deep voice. "Far's I'm concerned, you can even go voodoo that little Amélie de Fourcheux right out'n her doll babies."

Instruction in the black arts was by no means the full extent of Grenadine's early education. Three times a week M. Polyphème Maladroit, an unfrocked professor, came to call. M. Maladroit had been formerly an instructor of highly bred young ladies in the use of precise Parisian French, the scherzos of Chopin, and sufficient mathematics to allow them to keep a ladylike tab on household expenses. A thin, long-nosed, spaniel-eyed gentleman, M. Maladroit had lost his custom ten years a-past, when M. Jean-Paul Brouillard, a testy banker, had come upon M. Maladroit in the study of M. Brouillard's home, where he was engaged to instruct little Felice Brouillard, aged eight, in the piano. M. Maladroit, instead, was instructing Mme. Mercedes Brouillard, aged twenty-six, in a more fundamental art. As a souvenir of the occasion M. Maladroit wore a slight limp, caused by a bullet in the behind. He was cut dead by the Creole gentry, and he pieced out a precarious living by teaching piano to young octoroons whose mamas were raising them for a decorous career in the back streets of New Orleans gentility. When occasionally M. Maladroit had taken a sip too many he was apt to weep as he fingered the piano, and as he wept he departed from the tinkling chords of European masters and fell into more primitive rhythms. It was said that M. Maladroit, when drunk and remorseful, could coax sounds out of a piano to make a preacher lay his Bible down.

Twice a week Honeysuckle Dampier, the octoroon mistress of Jules Lenoir, the richest young buck in town, stopped by Maman Toddy's little house to give Grenadine lessons in how to be a fascinating female. She taught the child the art of subtle perfumes, of sly tricks of makeup, of dress and deportment. Grenadine was so busy that she rarely had time to play with her pet gorilla, which was just as well, because Brandy was getting older and more surly by the minute.

By the time Grenadine was nine years old she was accomplished in voodoo, the piano — both classical and New Orleans — and in the wiles of women thrice her age. Having displayed a keen and unchildish interest in mathematics, she had teased M. Maladroit into teaching her integral calculus and trigonometry. She spoke French, Spanish, Creole patois, English, and German fluently. She had a smattering of astronomy, chemistry, and jujitsu.

On her ninth birthday she became a woman; on her fifteenth she fell in love.

Becoming a woman was easy enough. Girls mature quickly and naturally in the South, and Maman Toddy was not surprised on Grenadine's birthday when the girl announced firmly: "Today, *Maman,* I am a woman, and intend to be treated as such."

At nine Grenadine looked eighteen. She had gained her full height of five feet ten inches. She was poker-straight, willow-slim, sun-bright, girl-faced, fresh-lipped, rose-cheeked, green-eyed, brown-eyed, and as lovely as a mint julep. Her breasts were small but firm and high, and her hips swayed with an unconscious allure. Her silver hair sparkled like water in the wind, like the sun on gulls' wings.

It was a soft June day, cool for New Orleans, and *Maman* was giving her a coming-of-age party. At fifteen Grenadine had passed her examinations with flying colors. To satisfy

Maman, she had caused, by judicious conversation with the spirits, the hair of Mme. Rolande Cochonmeme, the rival sorceress across the river in Algiers, to fall. For an encore she made Mme. Rolande's teeth drop out and her cows to miscarry their calves.

As a gracious gesture to her professor, M. Maladroit, she fabricated a simple incantation that induced M. Brouillard, the banker, to contract an odious disease as he dallied with a serving maid. Thieves broke into M. Brouillard's bank and made off with considerable funds, and that very day Felice Brouillard ran away with a feeble-witted gardener of unknown antecedents.

Maman Toddy, smiling all over her big black face, pronounced her a *maîtress* of the evil arts and graduated her *cum laude;* which is to say, Maman Toddy allowed her to mix her own juju powders. Grenadine's eyes glistened with childish glee at the accolade.

To satisfy her professor, she sat down at the piano and played Chopin's "Polonaise," a Bach fugue, a selection from Wagner's *Tannhäuser,* and "My Mamma Played a Harpsichord in a Ginmill" — a ditty very popular at the time among the frequenters of waterfront cafes. She propounded a mathematical formula to show that the cube root of x, if magnified to the eighteenth power, was indisputably y minus alpha, if subjected to a constant pressure under beta conditions. Giggling as she looked through her toy telescope, she discovered a new planet, which is called Etching's Planet to this day by the old stagers around the levees. Demonstrating her jujitsu, she threw Brandy, the gorilla, three out of three falls and was barely perspiring at the finish. Brandy, sulking at the disgrace, cowered behind the house, and in a fit of pique snapped the heads off three rabbits and a small German shepherd dog.

The hardest test had been to satisfy Honeysuckle, since instruction in women's wiles has no definite yardstick by which proficiency may be measured. Suffice to say that after Grenadine had stopped a stranger in the street and kissed him full on the lips, she passed the test. The stranger reeled, staggered, sat down by the side of the road, and began to chew his walking cane into small bits.

Maman Toddy made the valedictory speech. It was simple and to the point.

"Ah done the best Ah could by this chile," she said. "Ah tried to teach her all Ah knows. Ah tried to get the professor to teach her all he knows, so she won't nevah have to hang her haid in polite society. Since women has to operate mostly with mens, Ah got Honeysuckle to teach Grenadine all *she* knows about mens, and ain't nobody alive knows more about mens than Honeysuckle." (Honeysuckle dipped her head, blushed slightly, and smiled appreciatively.)

"Honey, you was born in sorrow and pain and death. You is a chile of death and commotion. You is a chile of struggle and hate, of mixed blood and unhappiness. You is part French and part Scotch and part Spanish, and maybe there is a little dark blood in yo' veins. When you come in this worl' yo' pappy was daid and yo' mammy was dyin'. The moon was black and drippin' with blood.

"Ah wants you to take this worl' by the tail and twist it till it hollers. When anythin' gets in yo' way, tromp it down and kick it out'n the way. When you needs a man to do yo' biddin', use him hard and cast him aside when you finish with him. Don't pay no mind to people that you can't bend to yo' whim. They ain't worth worryin' about, because they is either so stupid they don't count, or else they is stronger than you, and you ain't got time to waste on fights you can't win.

"You is 'quipped to take care of yo'self from now on better than most grown women—better than most mens. Step hard, walk proud, and move fast, honey. And don't leave nothin' in yo' path that you can't jump over or kick out'n the way. That's all Ah got to say, honey. Now, le's everybody have a little somethin' to keep out the chills."

It was a strange party. Besides Maman Toddy, Grenadine, M. Maladroit, Honeysuckle, and the pet gorilla, a variety of guests had been asked. There was Antoine Billingsley, a half-breed Indian who ran the town's toughest gambling casino with an iron hand. With Billingsley were both Conti brothers, Richard and Robert, tall, hard-eyed men, who spoke softly and drank hard. The elder brother, Richard, a demoniac drinker as a rule, always went on the wagon for a week after killing a man. It was significant, at this party, that he refused champagne and drank Vichy water. Another member of New Orleans' lamplit world, Mr. Clutch Thrasher, sat quietly in a corner, drinking slowly from a magnum of champagne (from which he had bitten the top), allowing the smoke from his cigar to curl around his moustaches, and never taking his dark, sad eyes from the guest of honor. Nobody knew much about Thrasher. He was a gambler. He seemed always to have plenty of money. He had killed three men in New Orleans, two with his hands and one with a horsewhip. Thrasher was a poet. He was fond, when riding alone on his black stallion, of declaiming Shakespeare's sonnets at the top of his lungs. The man he killed with the horsewhip had made the mistake of laughing at Thrasher who, engrossed in his poesy, had ridden his horse through the door of a café. Thrasher cut him to pieces with the whip, a sixteen-foot lash of bull hide tipped with brass, with which Thrasher could (and often did) snuff the ashes from a friend's cigar without disturbing the burning tobacco.

It was said of Thrasher that he had been a newspaper editor in the East, and that as a stripling of twenty-five he had wielded a smoking pen, which branded unmercifully too many vested interests in a corrupt city. One such captain of industry, enraged at an editorial, had stormed into the young editor's office with a gun. In the scuffle the outraged subscriber was shot four times through the left eye, and a jury, puzzled at this close grouping of wounds, found Thrasher guilty of murder. Rumor was that the judge's wife found means of providing the young writer with the key to his cell, traveling money, and a train ticket. This, of course, was the usual gossip surrounding gamblers who had dashing moustaches, sad brown eyes, and a tendency to pinch the seats of pretty girls.

Mme. Shoofly Ramirez, in whose house Maman Toddy had served an early apprenticeship, was there. Mme. Ramirez had retired, so to speak, and owned a block of business buildings, a small plantation just outside the city, a paddle-wheel steamboat, and a strongbox full of broad gold coins. She was in the best of health, and her illegitimate son, Renaldo Ramirez, had just been elected mayor of New Orleans. Mme. Shoofly Ramirez, who weighed three hundred pounds and had long black hairs growing from the corners of her mouth, was a living monument to the wisdom of frugality, temperance, and honesty.

The party, even for opulent New Orleans, was something

special. Maman Toddy had spared neither time nor expense
to guarantee that her ward's coming-out party would be, as
the current expression ran, "something out'n dis worl'."

For those who liked to dabble with the puncheon there
was brandy, Scotch whiskey, champagne, eggnog, port wine,
sherry wine, Rhine wine, Sauterne, Beaujolais, and something called casually dago red. There was absinthe, rum, gin,
vermouth (both sweet and dry), rye, bourbon, a variety of
the better blends. There was curaçao, crème de cacao,
aquavit, schnapps, eau-de-vie, muscat, and Triple Sec. There
was a punch compounded of all these ingredients, thickened
with ginger ale and fruit juices, which was called "Scorpion's
Tongue" and which Grenadine was allowed to taste, the better to familiarize her with the strong drink. It is to her
credit, or rather to the credit of her healthy young stomach,
that she managed to remain erect after drinking a cupful.

The broad oaken table in *Maman's* dining room creaked,
groaned, sagged, and trembled simultaneously with the
weight of the midnight supper, which had been in process of
construction for six weeks. There were, of course, the standard New Orleans dishes: jambalaya, cold shrimps with sauce
remoulade, trout marguery, trout à l'Arnaud, gumbo, ten-
derloin steaks, oysters prepared lovingly with spinach, oysters raw, oysters broiled, boiled, baked, and fricasseed; there
were frogs' legs from the bayous, quail, guinea hen, tender
young peacock, turkey, fried chicken, stewed chicken, and
broiled chicken. There was a ham of peccary topped with sea
gulls' eggs, a special compote of newts' tongues, doves'
tongues, and puff-adder tongues, a savory mess much esteemed in the locality.

There were shirred eggs à la Jeanne Lafitte and mashed

potatoes Andrew Jackson. There was a huge platter of shoo-fly pie, with its accompanying rashers of apple pandowdy. With the scrapple crop just harvested, each guest had individual plates of this tender delicacy, as well as basins of red and black caviar, whole anchovies, and tiny, succulent little octopuses.

Piled abundantly on the sideboards were apples, peaches, grapes, cherries, plums, nectarines, oranges, bananas, guavas, grapefruit, blackberries, quinces, sparkle-berries, and papayas. For dessert there was a choice of deep-dish apple pie, deep-dish ice cream, deep-dish blueberry pie, deep-dish plum tart, deep-dish éclairs, deep-dish profiteroles, deep-dish Baked Alaska, deep-dish crêpes suzette, and *deep*-dish *deep-dish,* a palate-tickling delicacy invented by the immortal New Orleans chef, M. Nonpariel Pappas.

In the words of Mme. Shoofly Ramirez, it was the goddamnedest repast ever set before man or beast and one of which Maman Toddy could be justly proud. This occurred to her later, when she was forced to throw it to the pigs, her guests having become too drunk to eat.

"But," she consoled herself, "it sho looked pretty settin' on the table."

Maman had spared no pains to provide music for her guests. She had hired four orchestras, which played in rotation. For comic relief there was Spike Hennessey and his Bayou Six, an orchestra composed of jugs, washboards, tin pans, and other assorted kitchenware. It is a matter of historical record that Mr. Hennessey later became governor of his state.

Following Mr. Hennessey was Miguelito Cohen and his talented array of *ñañigo* musicians, who played weird songs compounded of slave croonings and fireside chants; music filled with the shake of gourds, the rattle of asses' jawbones, the night noises of the swamplands, and the slow, pulsing beat of hidden orgies far from the view of the white man. Señor Cohen, a Spanish Jew, had fled his native Barcelona as a boy. He had lived in barbaric Rio de Janeiro as a young man and had come to New Orleans with a shipload of smuggled Chinese.

Hot on the heels of Señor Cohen was the seventy-piece orchestra of M. Armagnac Lombardi, which played softly, slowly, and sweetly. The succeeding and final band was a five-piece organization belonging to Marcel "Fats" Pichon, a coal-black pianist. M. Pichon was accompanied by two trumpeters, a drummer, and a thumper of the bass viol, and was easily the hit of the evening with spirited selections then popular around the levees.

Altogether there was no lack of music to keep the fete makers' feet tapping as they drank. As Mme. Ramirez remarked from time to time with delicious wit, "Even if they ain't good, they plenty loud."

Afterward nobody was quite sure how the trouble began. As the strong drink mounted to the heads of the guests the party began to get out of hand. The two Conti brothers, fired by whiskey, competed for the favors of Mlle. Honeysuckle Dampier and wound up by beating each other into a bloody pulp. This was nothing new for the Conti brothers; where they used guns on strangers, they used fists on each other. It was part of their pact against the world. They subsided, finally, into the rhododendrons in the side yard, there to sleep happily, if bloodily, until morning. They missed, as a matter of fact, the main event.

There were other brief highlights to the evening's wassail. Mr. Billingsley attempted to fondle Aurélie Brouillard, a pretty quadroon girl, with his iron fist, and was promptly knocked unconscious by Mlle. Brouillard, who wielded a heavy lamp. M. Maladroit, the professor, passed completely out while chasing Persephone Maintenon, the housemaid, round and round the kitchen table. He woke next morning in Persephone's bed, thoroughly disgusted.

All through the bacchic revel Grenadine moved slowly and regally, drinking little, bestowing her smile first on this guest, then on that. She was wearing a gown that, although her years were only fifteen, was calculated to rouse tumult in male breasts. It was of soft green velvet flecked with gold, the exact color of her eyes. Her snowy shoulders were bare and her proud young bosom half exposed. Her shimmering hair was piled high atop her head, and she walked fluidly on six-inch heels.

As she danced with guest after guest, Thrasher the gambler never took his eyes off her. Drinking steadily, he sat in one corner, lighting one cigar from the butt of another, devouring the young woman with his cold eyes. Finally, moistly warm from dancing, Grenadine walked to the veranda for a breath of the flower-laden air, and Thrasher uncoiled his long length to follow.

The cicadas were throbbing in the trees, and inside the house the aphrodisiac music of Cohen's Latin orchestra was throbbing too. Grenadine was throbbing inwardly as the cool air poured over her bare shoulders, and behind her Thrasher also throbbed. The warm, funky smell of earth mingled with the fragrance of mimosa, gardenia, and Thrasher's cigar. Grenadine strolled slowly into the yard, stepping over the inert bodies of the Frères Conti, and walked to her favorite spot beneath the magnolia tree. Through the night Thrasher's still, cold face yearned after her, and as a man bemused he silently followed. He dropped his whip on the grass.

The mist was wreathing ghostlike among the trees now, and the girl's face, bathed in moonlight, shone palely serene above the mist, as if disembodied. Thrasher's bodyless face, glowing evilly under the moon, suddenly appeared before her.

"Oh," she said. "You frightened me."

His dark eyes gleamed and his lips were wet as he reached for her. His long arms wrapped around her body, and placing a leg behind hers, he tripped her. As she sank to the damp grass his body covered hers. She struggled, but only momentarily.

Later, quivering, grass-stained, and pale as death, Grenadine crept into the house. Her mind was white as the fog that now had dropped, her body an inferno of raging emotion, her dress torn, and her hair fallen down. In the distance the hoofbeats of Thrasher's black horse were rapidly diminishing. She went to her bedroom and called softly to Maman Toddy.

"Send everybody home, Mammy," she said. "It's happened."

The woman twisted her hands.

"Ah knowed it would, Ah knowed it would," she said. "It was Thrasher?"

"Yes, Mammy," Grenadine said, hunched into a miserable knot on the bed.

"You wait heah," said Maman Toddy, "whilst Ah get rid of the guests."

Striding into the room where the guests still roistered, Toddy raised her voice.

"Break it up," she said. "Party's over. Mah baby sick. Musta been somethin' she drank. We'll see you kids nex' week."

Returning, she faced the girl on the bed.

"You got to kill him," she said flatly.

"I don't want to kill him," Grenadine answered. "I like him. I liked what he did to me. It was — it was — wonderful. Is that love, Mammy?"

"Fo' rattlehaided little gals it's love. Fo' you it ain't love. You got too much befo' you git tied down to some no-good gamblin' floater. Ah swear to John, sometimes Ah don't understand you, honey. Even in New Orleans gals ain't supposed to enjoy gettin' raped."

"But I love him," Grenadine repeated. "I don't want to kill him. I want —— "

"Don't make no nevermind," Toddy said. "You got to kill him."

"Why don't you do it?"

"It ain't up to me. The cards don't run thataway. It ain't in the book for me to kill him. The signs say you gonna fall in love and kill a man on the same night, and Thrasher is the man. Get up and put on yo' spo't clothes. This ain't no job for a gal in a long dress that's tight around the feet."

"Yes, ma'am," Grenadine said.

"You got the gun?" *Maman* asked as they walked down Royal Street.

"I got it," Grenadine said. "It's loaded. Whose is it, anyhow?"

"Don't fret yo' pretty haid about whose is it," Maman

Toddy answered. "Fella I know brought it back from the war. Bought it off'n a prisoner for a twist o' tobacco. Ain't no serial number on that gun. Not no local serial number, anyhow."

A light glowed greenly from the window of Thrasher's apartment four floors up. The iron door leading into the building was locked.

"Shhhh," Maman Toddy said. "Gimme a second."

Her fingers passed rapidly over the lock. In a trice she tossed something over her shoulder into the grass and the door swung open.

"Take it from heah," she said to Grenadine.

Grenadine slowly mounted the stairs. Her heart pounded like a prisoned bird fluttering against her skin. She tapped timidly on the door. Thrasher's voice answered her rap — answered dimly, a weary voice.

"It's me," she said. "I have to see you."

The door opened, and she gasped as she saw the gambler's face. It had aged immeasurably. It was gray and flabby, and the beard was greenish-black around his sagging jowls. His bloodshot eyes stared dully from brown pouches; his hair fell raggedly over his forehead. The room reeked of smoke and cheap whiskey. All of a sudden Grenadine felt sick.

I know now why Mammy said I had to kill him, she murmured to herself. *I hate myself for what I let him do.*

"What do you want?" Thrasher asked. "What are you doing here at this hour?" And, wildly, "Will I never find peace? Will no woman ever give me peace?"

"I will," Grenadine said, shooting him precisely in the navel. The boom of the gun was deafening in the small room.

"But why? why?" Thrasher, his face bent by agony, asked from the floor. "Why did you do it?"

"My *maman* done tole me," Grenadine answered simply, her face a stark mask.

She squeezed the trigger again, and Thrasher the gambler died on the floor. It developed much later, when the police attempted to find a claimant for the remains, that he had a wife and five children in Jackson Heights, New York. Actually, it was not yet named Jackson Heights, but the locality was the same. The wife refused to accept his body, and Thrasher the gambler was planted locally in the dank plot of ground reserved for gamblers.

This, however, is parenthetical. Grenadine, wiping the gun free of prints, tossed it on the floor.

"Good-bye," she said. "Good-bye, my first love."

"You done it," Maman Toddy said. "But how come you had to shoot twice?"

"I hit him a little low the first time," Grenadine answered, biting her lips until they bled. "This ain't — isn't — too easy for a girl, *Maman.*"

"Ah know, honey, but women's lives is full of pain and sorrow. You got to do what you got to do. And now we gonna excape to Havana, Cuba. It's gonna be hard but necessary."

"But why? Why? What's the use of it all? Why can't we stay here? Why do we have to go to Cuba?"

"It's in the script," Maman Toddy said. "By dat Ah mean like what the Arabs say — 'Kismet.' When you gotta go you gotta go, and we gotta go to Cuba."

"But I don't want to go to Cuba," Grenadine wailed. "I didn't want to shoot Thrasher, I want ——"

"Don't make no nevermind what you want," Toddy said firmly. "We headin' for Havana. Sometimes I loses patience with you, chile. Even dead gamblers raise some kind of stink in New Orleans, and I purely don't want no cops prowlin' round my house. Cuba we goes to, and early in the mornin'. Mammy knows best."

"Yes, Mammy," Grenadine said meekly, wondering inchoately what the future held, and if she must always be a pawn of fate, or authors.

PART FOUR

Uncle Robert's Bedtime Stories and Other Happenings

Once Upon A Time — *and* — They Lived Happily Ever After — *have fascinated old and young for as many years as any old and young can remember. It was no less so with Ruark, who parodied a few as a diversion from his continuing fight with the world of women. He called them bedtime stories; the lead character, as in the originals, was always a girl.*

Cinderella

Cinderella was a cute little doll who played a type-writer for thirty-five dollars a week in an advertising agency. She lived in a walk-up railroad flat with a passel of sisters, including two hip models. There was a wicked old mother-in-law too, left over from one of the sister's early, brief matrimonial venture with a Harvard man.

Cinderella was a nice little dish, if you like 'em mousy, but she was always flat broke, what with trying to eat, pay rent, dress, and take care of her sisters on thirty-five fish before the withholding tax.

The model-type sisters didn't work much, and when they did, they put the dough on their backs. And the old lady never turned a hand. Just sat there, reading two-bit detective stories and griping about the service.

If groceries got bought, it was apt to be Cinderella who bought them, and when the man came around for the rent, it was generally Cindy who dug into her darned nylons and produced same. This left her very little dough for new clothes or the beauty parlor, and a dime a day was the best she could spend on lunch. She got pretty shabby.

She was sitting in the ladies' lounge one day, sniffling into the Kleenex and wishing that her luck would change, when one of the other stenos came in and said she was quitting, but had recommended Cindy for a job in the big boss's office. It wasn't long before the big boss, a kindly old fellow, saw the pure gold beneath Cinderella's drab bolero, and he rigged a project.

One of the clients — a beer account — wanted a demure, sweet girl to pose for one year as Miss Steinblatz, and Cindy filled the bill. All she needed was clothes. They fixed that in a hurry.

They took her to Hattie's for gowns, and Delman did her shoes, and Mister John whipped up her hats. They sent her to the charm school and she came out sharp as a tack. Antoine built her a special hairdo. They raised her pay, and all she had to do was hold still for the photographer. The photographer was young, handsome, and, oddly enough, an American citizen.

Well, it was a steady party for Cinderella, with Cadillacs waiting at the door and caviar and champagne at El Morocco and all like that.

But one day the boss man made her a proposition, involving a Park Avenue apartment and a midget French poodle; and being a good girl, Cinderella said no. In two days they had reclaimed all the fancy clothes and costume jewelry and fired her, besides. The sisters and the old lady raised Cain when she told them.

Well, sir, Cinderella was back in the walk-up sewer, crying in a corner, when in walks the photographer. He says he has been thinking it over, and no other girl's face will ever fit his camera as well as Cinderella's. Although the two model sisters tried to muscle in, he left with our Cindy tucked under his arm.

They get married, Cindy poses — in between babies —

and by and by they buy their own studio. They are as happy as ever they can be. I can't tell you what became of the mean sisters and the cruel old woman, because Cinderella never goes back to that Third Avenue flat. She figures she had served her apprenticeship, and baby-sitters are hard to come by.

Sleeping Beauty (and the Goofballs)

Once upon a time there was a lovely whom everybody called The Princess. Her old man, J. Pierpont Cartel, the Third, was called The King, because he owned a controlling interest in tobacco, tinplate, automobiles, whiskey, and Congress. One day The King kicked off, due to gout, and left The Princess as sole custodian of all that gelt.

The Princess was as pretty as a thousand-dollar bill. She had a 36-inch chest and likewise hips, and she had a million bucks a week to spend. It was natural for The Princess to attract a constant quorum of eager young men, who loved her for herself and who wished to document their affection with a preacher.

One thing worried The Princess. All those young men were handsome and polished. They could do a magnificent rumba, but they all seemed to be strictly from no skins, which is an archaic phrase meaning flat busted. The Princess didn't know for sure whether they loved her true, or maybe was it the Connecticut estate or the Honolulu ranch or the Palm Beach villa or the castle in Italy or the New York quadruplex, or the beach house in Cannes. It preyed on her mind considerable.

The Princess went off her feed. She was snappish with the help, began to bash the booze around a bit, and took to smoking before breakfast. One night, after she wobbled in from a dizzy round of dancing dens, she pulled the ermine blanket under her chin and closed her eyes. But she kept seeing things on the ceiling, and hearing funny little frog noises, until by and by she was terrified. With her nerves crawling, The Princess reached shakily over to the night table and clawed up a handful of goofballs, or sleeping pills. She was accustomed to belting herself over the head with these pills on her white nights, so this time she up and swallowed a fistful.

Next morning, when the maid came in with the plover hearts and powdered pearls, on which The Princess normally breakfasted, the poor little rich girl was still out cold. Yvonne hollered for the butler, and he hollered for the footman, and the footman hollered for the head chauffeur, and they lugged The Princess off to the bridal suite of a hospital. She was still snoring like a pig in the sun.

A whole covey of the best croakers in town came and worked her over; the Sleeping Beauty wouldn't come to. She just lay there, making bubbly sounds, for week after week. They had to feed her intravenously to keep her alive. With her eyes squeezed shut, she occasionally muttered "money," and then started to snore again. Three weeks later, her chief sawbones (Dr. Basil Métabolisme, the noted French diagnostician who had planed in from Paris) desperately summoned a psychiatrist.

"We have exhausted science," said Dr. Métabolisme.

"Alors, now we try magic." The psychiatrist took one look at the girl and nodded his head.

"Obviously," he said, "she is traumatic in the syndromes, or vice versa, and suffers from a block. I will treat her subconsciously."

After six months, he had arrived at the seat of the trouble. "The Princess," said he, "has too much money. It makes her feel insecure. She is retreating from reality in sleep. Time will cure her."

The treatment went on for years, at Lord knows how much the séance. The Princess's fortune melted until finally she was stony broke. As the last dollar dwindled, she smiled, yawned, stretched, and woke. Her eyes lit on the hospital orderly, and twenty minutes later they had eloped through the window. He was a very handsome orderly.

Oh, sure, he belted her around some when he discovered she was no longer loaded, but The Princess was no crow, and marriage ripened into love. Today they are poor but very happy. However, the odd footnote was this, kiddies: Shortly after effecting the cure, the spade-bearded psychiatrist fell into a coma and has been snoring his head off ever since. His colleagues say he has too much money, and it makes him feel insecure.

Beauty and the Beast

Beauty was the youngest of three daughters. Beauty's old man was a speculator in cotton and wheat futures. All the girls were pretty, but Beauty was a killer. When she won her first beauty contest, at the age of two, everybody said she would go far.

Our girl friend was about fourteen, and the other sisters were young ladies, when the old man overreached himself in the commodity market and went for his wad. What wheat didn't get, cotton did, and Beauty's papa was stranded without a buck to bless himself with.

The two sisters didn't care, because they'd been fluttering around in society, and they figured to take up the option on a couple of willing boyfriends with dough in the bank. But a funny thing: soon as Father blew his roll, the rich boys went off and started courting some fresh talent.

These sisters moaned and groaned and yearned for riches, but that's all they did.

Beauty never quit trying. She worked in the five-and-dime all day, and all evening long she practiced accomplishments. She learned to tap-dance. She learned to shake her shoulders and sell a torch song. She practiced speaking in front of the mirror, and the neighbors all thought she was nuts, because she walked around for hours with an encyclopedia on her head.

At sixteen, she was elected Miss North Wilkes-Barre. At seventeen she was chosen Miss Pennsylvania. She was Miss Slagpit, Miss Scrapple, and Miss Mushroom on successive years. When she turned twenty-one she came to Atlantic City and was chosen Miss America. By this time she was a knockout. She had eyes like Vivien Leigh, legs like Betty Grable, a torso like Jane Russell, and a mind like a steel trap. Beauty went to Hollywood.

She went under contract to a big studio, but for peanuts, and she never got a chance to act. All she did was pose for publicity stills and assorted cheesecake for the fan magazines. She used to cry in the Brown Derby every night, as she munched her frugal meal of Ry-Krisp and milk. One night, as she was crying, a huge, gross man with a wart on his nose stopped by her table.

"I am Morris J. Mannerheim, the producer at Stupendous Studios," he said. "May I help you?"

"Yes," Beauty said automatically (she had been in Hollywood a long time). Then she looked up and gasped, because Morris J. Mannerheim was the ugliest man she had ever seen. He looked like Lon Chaney with overtones of Gargantua. The employees on the Stupendous lot always called him The Beast.

The Beast was very kind to Beauty. He took her everywhere. He bought up her contract and signed her to a seven-year term with Stupendous at $100,000 a year. He cast her in the female lead of every picture he produced. He smothered her with furs and gems.

The day she finished her first picture, they were married. She moved into his Belair mansion, and sent for her father and sisters that very day. In two years Beauty was acclaimed a star in her own right, and her contract rectified to call for two pictures a year at a cool quarter million each.

Then Beauty met Brentwood Beamish, who worked for Repulsive Studios. He was the hottest thing since Valentino, and every time he sighed, nine thousand women shot their husbands. After Brentwood, The Beast seemed to get uglier and uglier.

The night she won her first Oscar, Beauty filed for divorce, charging mental cruelty, citing her husband's face as Exhibit A. Under California law, she got half his property, including the big house at Belair and the little one at Palm Springs, plus a cash settlement of $500,000. Beauty married Brentwood the next day, and The Beast drank himself to death in six months.

There is a moral, children. It's just that if you're beautiful, intelligent, and industrious, you can always find some chump who'll make you rich and famous. A strong stomach helps, too.

A Good-bye Girl

This little girl, named Gisele, is not the heroine of a bedtime story, but she seems to belong in a dream where the setting is clear but the protagonist is only dimly remembered.

Tommy was a cross between Errol Flynn and Freddie McEvoy, combining the best and worst qualities of each, looking like both and living like a corporation embracing both. It is doubtful if his name actually *was* Tommy Thomson, but he was an authentic Scot. I met him in Tangier a great many years ago, when Tangier was as wicked as its reputation. At that time he was a smuggler. He smuggled anything you could smuggle, from cigarettes to whiskey to kef and, I suspect, women. He smuggled by way of Gibraltar and Majorca to mainland Spain, mostly. He had his own schooner — a boat as long as Flynn's *Sirocco* — and his associates were two ex-Nazis on the lam, one half-bred English gentleman, an itinerant Turk, a snub-nosed Irish refugee, an Australian faggot, and two Lesbians, only one of whom was French. His company also included a couple of Arabs with their hands in the customs, a purely formal function that only served to facilitate movement of contraband from a duty-free city to other lands in which whiskey and cigarettes commanded premium prices.

Tommy was a gambler, and one night I saw him win a fourteen-year-old Arab girl in a poker game. Her name was Leila Nakhla, and she was very pretty, if slightly pocked from either an old family inheritance or a recently acquired malaise. (Tommy lost her a few weeks later to a former British chorus boy who called himself Count Something-or-other. A king full beat Tommy's queen full, but he made up the deficit with an arrangement of hashish candy.)

I saw Tommy in Monte Carlo, in the casino, well before the Greeks bought it, and he was with a very pretty French girl. I offered a small hello — a very small hello, because I never did know when Tommy was operating big and I never wanted to become an irritant when he *was* operating big. For all I knew, Tommy was about to marry into the shipping business — or open his own casino with an anticipated largess.

"Joseph!" Tommy gave me the big warm hand. "Come meet my girl friend. This is Mademoiselle — what was the name again, *ma chérie?*"

"Gisele," *ma chérie* said, and Tommy shrugged.

"Gisele and I just met. And I have stopped gambling. I took a pretty good clobber at the tables in the last month. Then I met Gisele and I am now taking her to dinner. Purely friendship. And no gambling. All I have is seventy pounds, because what I had left after the clobbering I sent back to England, where soon I shall join it."

"A stupid question, perhaps," I said. "But if you're not gambling, what are you doing here in the casino?"

Again Tommy shrugged.

"You know how it is. Sentimental gesture. Twenty quid buys dinner and gets me out of town. So with my remaining fifty I shall have the one final throw. This is kind of a self-cure. I'm going to miss the clicking sound when the croupier says, '*Rien ne va plus,*' and that dirty little ball falls into a slot. But I am going straight. I might even go to work. This is what you might call a farewell to arms. For last luck, the lass gets half."

He turned to the girl.

"Gisele, *quel âge avez-vous?*"

"I am twenty-four," the girl said. She was not such a one as you would expect to find out on the night with Tommy Thomson, unless he was about to leave town with no future in the arrangement. This was a good-bye girl if I ever saw one.

"Well," Tommy said, "do me a favor, Joseph. Hold my

twenty pounds, and we shall give it one last riffle on Gisele's age with the fifty. If twenty-four comes up, we will have roughly two thousand pounds as a souvenir of this lovely principality. A kiss for luck, *chérie. Garçon!* A drink for my friends!"

Tommy walked over to the roulette board and looked at it as though he were about to shoot his dog, his horse, and his mother.

"Don't molest yourself with chips," he said to the banker. "Just put the fifty pounds on number twenty-four. For luck. It is the age of the lady."

"*C'est très romantique,*" the croupier said, before he spun the wheel. "Betting fifty pounds on a lady's age." The ball bobbled, then came to rest. *Rouge. Numéro* 28.

Another shrug from Tommy.

"This just isn't my year," he said. "Let's have a spot of haggis before I chase the plane."

I looked at *chérie.* She was crying, the mascara was dripping. Fifty pounds is only fifty pounds, and I figured she well might better this score in two nights of honest toil. Women are very unattractive when they cry in public.

Tommy looked at her as if she were some species of bug.

"I lost five thousand quid this week," he said. "What's to cry over about a lousy fifty when I've quit gambling anyhow?"

"But *I lied, I lied, I lied!* My age is actually *twenty-eight!* And I told you I was only *twenty-four!*"

Tommy looked at me and shrugged for the fourth time.

"Sweetie," he said, "you just blew half of two thousand pounds, according to the odds on the number." Then, to me: "Give me the twenty back."

I gave him the money. He peeled off two fives. Then he turned to the girl: *"Ma chérie.* This will get you home. But for God's sake, remember that a gambler is not interested in anything but vital statistics."

He turned to me. "You travel a lot, Joseph. What is your recommendation for the best hamburger joint in Prince Rainier's province?"

A Thousand Dollars a Week

The image of Amelia is clear from two graphic letters she wrote from a health farm. She is a typical Ruark heroine — witty, caustic, striving all the time to keep her place in his gallery of beauties. But that "uncertain age" feeling is creeping up, and she cannot afford to slip. What she has to do, in fact, is afford the drastic treatment it takes not to.

Dear Svengali:

Out of solitary and one of the wardens lent me a pen and some paper. I don't know if you really realize what goes on in these places, for a thousand a week, so for lack of anything better to do, I'll tell you. First off, you'll never recognize me. They have jacked up the old chassis and run a new car underneath it. Or so it feels.

Before you so blithely advise another friend to take the cure the hard way, you had better know something about what goes on inside these walls, so I'll give you the play-by-play.

To go alone is very *déclassé*. It appears I am very *déclassé*. I should have brought you.

It *is* expensive. Maybe a thousand dollars a week. Haven't got to the tips yet. Everybody too well-bred to mention money. We live in little groups of houses around the main building, which is the central station. At least I'm not lonesome.

First they check your own doctor's papers and give you a physical exam. Next they establish a sort of regime for you. If you're here to lose weight, and who ain't, it goes more or less like this:

They get us up at dawn. They issue us darling little peach-colored shifts, which are very short and belted loosely so that you betray very damn little of your basic girth. Everybody wears same outfit like in girls' school. Run around in sandals which are also GI. Seems if you're a good little girl you get to keep these. Goody-two-shoes-five-hundred-bucks apiece!

Breakfast consists of "simply delicious" fruits and juices and black coffee or tea. The fruits are all fresh and clean and lovely and homegrown on the premises. The gardener wears a surgeon's mask to keep them pure. It is a very filling breakfast. If you like breakfast. As you know, I *hate* breakfast.

Next we have an exercise period — big group deal. Everybody lies down on spotless mats (peach again) while music plays and a lovely, skinny female (*hate* her) gives directions for rolling for the hips, and sit-ups for flattening the tummy. We do this a little longer each day, but basically it *never* gets any better.

Everything we eat is lightly salted, and there is no sodium chloride on the table. Outwardly, we are losing weight like mad, but mostly it is just stored water. Football players can lose up to ten pounds of this excess water in one game, they tell us. But we are not football players.

Now we have a mid-morning break for refreshments. This is either tomato juice or various teas made of old gumshoes or possibly even imported exotic seaweed, depending upon what PARTICULAR kick our all-knowing doctor is on. The seaweed tea has great snob value. It tastes like castor oil.

After the juice-*cum*-tea break we go swimming, but under strict supervision. Miss La Roache takes us to the big, over-heated pool, where we thoughtfully do so many breast strokes to build up our flabby pectoral muscles, etc. We wear caps. We look *awful*. We wear issue swim suits which are sloppily pleated and Neo-Grecian in derivation, and which do not betray our figures unless we are absolutely soaked. In this case, we cannily observe one another from the corners of the eyes, but we refrain from comment. We are in NO position to criticize. We are all in this mess together.

We do the swim thing the easy hard way. Sometimes we just flutter-kick fifty times slowly, so as not to exhaust us, while we hang onto the side of the pool. Drowning is frowned on by the management.

After the swim we might have a brief game of badminton, but this is optional, like cancer. Most of us choose the shower and change into our peachy shifts (short and Grecian, with peach ballet tights beneath), but leisurely. About this time I would *maim* for a Martini; KILL for a Bloody Mary.

Oh *boy!* Now comes lunch. Vegetables, demi-cooked, or revoltingly raw with a low-calorie, health-giving dressing based largely on tomato juice, spices, and mineral oil.

For your information, sweetie, mineral oil has wonderful

laxative qualities, but it also has a tendency to *leak* when least expected.

We have next a free period in which we can take a nature walk or just lie in bed and gossip about WHO IS HERE NOW. This is very important. It is dreadful to be here the week AFTER the Duchess of Windsor and the week BEFORE Mamie Eisenhower. It is like Russian roulette to hit the right week.

Next there is the treatment, or therapy session. It varies. The resort urges you take the mud bath for YOUR PARTICULAR PROBLEM. Treatments are fairly grim. For one thing, a maiden lady might just get a male *masseuse*. It is true that he uncovers only one area at a time, and (honest!) never gets what you would call *fresh*. But it is mostly the idea of having a male rub you the wrong way that really rubs you the wrong way.

There are all sorts of possibilities in this therapy racket, but mostly it is pretty damn dull. Goes like this:

1. *The steam cabinet or mudpack.*
   In either event it is hotter than the human flesh can stand and we sweat off absolutely POUNDS of FAT, darling! (Or is it that goddam accumulated water?)
2. *The massage.*
   This is where you get pummeled by a Swiss or Swede who speaks hardly a word of English, so that it will be embarrassing later to go home to your husband covered head to toe with bruises because the goddam *masseuse* couldn't comprehend when I said, "Goddamit, you're breaking my back."
3. *The rest period.*
   It makes us nervous to lie in the booth with the cur-

tain only, and no lock. The table is hard and it doesn't
quite fit, no matter which way we turn, because in
spite of our natural overstuffing the bones have a way
of digging into the thinly padded leather table, or
vice versa. At some point we doze off.

4. *The shower.*

Brisk and cold. We dry. We put on our peachy short
shifts, and then pad back to our cottages in time to
change for cocktails and dinner.

Cocktails and dinner are full dress, and done properly by
candlelight, which softens the wrinkles. Now — for reducers, there might be choices of sauerkraut juice, tomato,
orange (grape is too high-cal), or any combination of fruits
and vegetables blended and strained. There is even something called The Elimination Cocktail. I can only assume it
has a prune-juice base.

We drink the cocktails from the cocktail-looking glasses.
You can have them straight like a Martini, or on the rocks,
or with water or soda. We stand around sipping and chatting
elegantly. We are wearing full evening regalia, and all our
genuine diamonds and pearls. No men are involved, except
possibly Dr. God up there who is the Physician of us all, and
who is SUCH a charmer. He told me this morning that he was
TERRIBLY pleased with my progress with my INNER THIGH
PROBLEM.

Now, sweetie, we stroll into the dinner room at the proper
time when the chimes *chime.* In twos and threes we stroll.
Leisurely. Trailing trains, flaunting plumes. We case one
another, which is to say: How much money can you wear at
one time and still maintain good taste? Also we are very

keen to track down the designers of each other's gowns. We sort of show off, like so:

"*Chanel* said it was perfect for me, but I never felt at home in it."

"I hate to confess it is three years old, but of course Charles James did it and He is timeless."

"You are so sweet to say so, but Trigère's one great fault is that you MUST hold your tummy *in*."

"Yes, it's a Rentner, but it hasn't fit right since the last baby — you just don't know what it's *like* to have a menopause baby . . . not that we don't just *adore* little Afterthought."

Dinner is formal. We are seated in groups according to our diets. Our reducers' group has lean meat, cooked vegetables (mostly stalks and leaves, because the roots have more carbohydrate), and salads. Sometimes we have fish. Always the sauces are excellent in a loathsome sort of way. They use a lot of herbs, lemon juice, and vinegar.

That's about the shape of it. I'll probably come out of here looking like Betty Grable — or at least like Betty Grable's mother.

Love,

    Trilby, formerly Amelia.

Three days later, there was another bulletin from the fighting fronts. It said:

Dear Pygmalion:

One would not recognize us girls by now. We are not women — we are *creations!* By now we have been completely created by the famous M. de Quatrefages himself who, lest you forget, absolutely eclipses Antoine, Michel, and Mr. Kenneth when it comes to hairstyles, skin care, beauty, and general inspiration.

Some of us pronounced Monsieur de Quatrefages correctly right from the beginning, but there is a certain element here that still fluffs the lines when it has to pronounce him. Quatrefages sounds very funny with a Houston accent.

He is not much to look at. He is dapper and brisk. The reason he is brisk is because he damn well *better* be brisk. He is highly paid to give PERSONAL attention to a number of us, and there are QUITE a number of us.

First there is the personal analysis, which is a pip. You are ushered into his private office, which is so austere you expect to be sterilized before sitting down — sprayed, maybe, like they used to do in airplanes. He sits behind a stern desk. He wears a black business suit to match his moustache and eyes. (And heart.) By contrast, you feel absolutely naked in your skimpy little peach shift. I keep tugging at the hem of mine.

A battery of lights like in the gangster movies is aimed at your face. *He* sits hidden in the gloom to study *you*. You are aware that his walls are covered with framed certificates, but God only knows what these are for — you never get a chance to read them. Probably vivisections.

"Do *not* speak," he says, holding up one finger, while he studies you. You immediately feel guilty, and a couple of little muscles around the mouth get absolutely taut and begin to hurt. My right eyelid develops a tic.

"Ah, Madame," he says finally, "you really have a *lovely* bone structure, and marvelously *malleable* features, but you haven't been taking *care* of yourself, now *have* you?" He shakes his head in a slow, meaningful negative, like a gynecologist pronouncing the loathsome truth.

You shake your head in shameful, childlike guilt. He is The Truth and The Light and can see *right* through *you*.

"It is very fortunate that we met before it's too *late*. We will put you *back on the track*. We will *reveal* your *hidden beauty*." And you know, all of a sudden, he's *right*. You got beauty you didn't know you had.

And so he begins to sketch, but you can't see *what* he is sketching. We suddenly realize the reason for Mona Lisa's smile — her mouth is twitching from sheer nervous exhaustion and cannot quite be captured.

"*Voici!*" cries M. de Quatrefages, turning his sketch pad over so that we can see. (I jumped a foot.) But it is really an expert likeness of my face, but totally *without* hair. It is the very ESSENCE OF ME in a glorified sort of way, but *without any hair at all!*

I defied Jovian wrath and mumbled: "A maybe sort of golden halo, please?"

He says, tut-tutting and shaking that goddam finger.

"Ah, but *madame*, you are *here* for ME to decide."

He hid the drawing from me again while he designed the new hair for Our Particular Type of Undisclosed Beauty. We strain to peer over the top of the pad, but he conceals it until he is finished.

"*Voici!*" he cries, and this time I only jumped six inches. He shows me the completed sketch with the new hairstyle. It is large, a full face from the front. Two smaller sketches near the bottom show the profile and rear view.

In my particular case it *is* a golden halo sort of thing.

Hurray! ¡Olé! It occurs to Very Damn Few of us that his every hairstyle is the EXACT OPPOSITE of our current style. It gives us HOPE.

He now writes my name under it like a title and signs his own just like an artist.

He then takes out my Personal Skin Care and Beauty Analysis Chart. And for the first time he really speaks — first of skin care, then of cosmetics. Studying me like some sort of bug, he puts checks on this chart, item by item, while he explains Our Problem in terms of Fat Flattery that would be outrageous if We weren't in such dire need of it. (Goddam that *We!*)

Wrinkles on the foreheard are mere "worry lines." Whaddaya know? All the time I thought it was sun.

"Ah, *madame,* life has not always been easy for you," he murmurs sympathetically. (He can say THAT again!) "But I can tell from the laugh lines about your eyes that always you have tried to keep the sense of humor — it is a part of your charming nature —" That sort of horseshit. *Laugh lines?* It is but to *weep.*

From the number of marks he makes on the chart, I'm going to need a ton of creams and cosmetics, but what the hell, kid, what the hell.

He even discusses Our Fingernail Polish Plight with a keen sense of deep understanding. Not to mention *compassion.* I actually was sorry when it all had to end. I felt like I'd been to *communion.*

He rings a bell to summon his first assistant in charge of all salons. Mlle. Lorette appears like a genie from a jar. They don't start to keep you waiting until after you've bought all the crap.

The Maestro indicates the sketches and the chart of new products. Mlle. Lorette regards these as if it is the first time ever she has seen anything so admirable. She then regards *me,* still floodlit, like a species of snake. She hardly can restrain her enthusiasm, but she manages.

He waves his hand in godlike dismissal. She leads us out into the main salon. I am still numb and half blind from the floodlights. I would confess to *anything.*

The salon is upholstered like the inside of a womb, to the best of my recollection of what wombs are like inside. It is peach-colored throughout, except for the actual fixtures they need for the hair. Even the fluorescent lights are peach-colored. We don't learn until MUCH later that an old survey (*circa* 1846) showed peach to be the most flattering of all colors to the human skin. Sometimes the wardens around here blab such secrets to the prisoners.

A maid ties us into a peach-colored smock while Mlle. Lorette waits (at what they must pay HER an hour!) to introduce us to M. Paul, our hair boy.

With the help of about twenty other people, M. Paul converts us into a *natural* blonde with a proper halo. His haircut is radical, but nothing like so bad as a hysterectomy. I'm pitifully pleased that he does the haircut, roll-up, and combout himself. Sometimes he turns clients over to an intern for these critical stages of the operation. Then EVERYBODY in the salon notices, and the client loses face, whoever she be.

Under the dryer, someone hands me a magazine to read. It is an elegant, glossy affair called *Connaissance*. It is entirely in French.

"They ASSUME that we read *le* French. The only French I

know is *bidet,* but I was afraid to ask for *Field & Stream.* I read *Connaissance.*

At the Grand Finale, M. Paul selects Our Particular Type of hair spray and lacquers the new hairdo into the hardness of a turtleshell over my suffering skull.

At this golden moment of completion, M. Paul hands us a looking glass, and suddenly M. de Quatrefages, Mlle. Lorette, and all the other imps magically materialize for a moment of prayer over the absolute Miracle of It All.

From the corner of my eye I note that M. de Q. gives a little bow to Our Newfound Beauty.

It is the same in the skin care and makeup parlor where M. R. Donald (U. S. citizen, whaddaya know) takes me in hand. Carefully following M. de Quatrefages' chart, he shows us our proper ritual for night and day. It will leave very little time for anything unimportant like sleeping and eating. He cleans the skin until the pores spout blood. Then he beautifies us. At the last he applies the new false eyelashes. They *itch.*

Again, at the finale, the entire staff pops out of the magic lantern. At this point I felt that M. de Quatrefages is absolutely inflamed by Our Newfound Beauty, and might just rape me behind the cosmetics counter. *He didn't.* Chicken.

It is the same with the skin care and makeup salon. It seems *We* need special face-muscle exercises to tighten up the lovely clean line of *Our* jaw so that *We* more nearly can approach the lean Katharine Hepburn type we really were destined to be until Something Went Wrong. We also must have *Our* daily facial to "tone" our tissues.

Although we have had abiding faith in Chanel No. 5 for

years, M. de Quatrefages has unsold us on it. It might just louse up the Total Effect of the Nu-*Us*.

In short, we have a new *parfum,* too. For Our Particular New Type.

Stand back! The Beauty is coming home!

Love,

Galatea

PART FIVE

The Girls
He Could Love

There were women in Ruark's life. He attracted, and was attracted to many in his time. They were varied in size and contour and way of life. He eulogized them in his stories, and no Ruark heroine was ever less than glamorous, humorous and desirable. Even walking away they left a sense of desire and nostalgia.

Among The Girls He Could Love are those who would fit into the pocket of any man with a roving eye. Every one of them is a composite picture of several, and each, despite an idealistic aura, is subject to human frailty.

There is THE MOVIE STAR, *Barbara, the red-blooded male's* and the press agent's dream. *For her there came one time, at least, when she was happy the cameras were not on her.*

Libby is THE GIRL BACK HOME, *who should have remained young, sweet, and innocent, especially in a small town in North Carolina.*

The Valerie episode may not be the last reel in the movie, but she represents all the girls who resolutely close the pages on a bad chapter to face life alone. Valerie is THE GIRL WHO WILL NEVER COME BACK.

Penny is THE NYMPHETTE, *the young thing that no middle-aged man in his right senses should fool with. But a man is often tempted, in this case by a charmer who doesn't give up, despite the rivalry of her mother for the same man's affections.*

And there is THE GIRL YOU FALL IN LOVE WITH IN WARTIME. *In this collection she is Sheila, and hers is a very special memory that will never fade.*

Barbara—The Movie Star

They managed three different flamenco caves after dinner, which ended at two thirty A.M. In each of the side-street cafés, faces lit when they entered, and the gypsies invariably said, *"¡Holà, Señorita Barbarà!"* Or simply, *"¡Olé Barbarà!"* In each of the places they visited, the *guitarristas* came immediately to the table to play what seemed to be carbon copies of her favorite songs. The singers, corded necks swelling like frogs' throats, yelled what also seemed to be her favorite songs. Twice, on loud demand, she got up to perform what appeared to Alec a very creditable flamenco, with loud handclappings and frequent *¡Olés!* and *¡Ay, qué tías!* from the performers as well as from the few dark men who rested against the bar and drank *manzanilla*. At the table, whole armies of bottles of *manzanilla* disappeared as the flamenco singers and guitarists produced private performances for Barbara, with glares of rebuke from the leader if a rival group started a song for another table in another part of the room.

It was five o'clock when Alec's yawns almost eclipsed the woody clack of the castanets.

"I done come a long way in the last twenty-four hours," he said finally. "I think we've had enough clicking and clacking for one night, wouldn't you say?"

Barbara looked at her wristwatch.

"My God! And I've got to be up at six! Well, there's no point in my going to bed now. You can buy me breakfast in another place I know, and then I'll just bathe and slip into my working duds. You want to go out on the set with me tomorrow — I mean this morning?"

"Great God, no." Alec yawned again. "All I want is to sling these creaky old bones into bed."

"My bed?"

Alec shook his head emphatically.

"Great God, no, again. What with the flying and the f——, the lovemaking and the food and the flamenco, I am what you might call 4-F at the moment. Take me back to the Trace, lead me to my room, and I will bolt the door. I aim to sleep twelve hours straight."

"You always did lack stamina," Barbara said. "Come on.

We'll skip the breakfast. I'll have tea and toast sent up to my room, and eat it while I dress."

"For this small boon I am indeed deeply grateful," Alec said. "I can take guitars with most meals, but not with breakfast."

Alec made one trip out to the set and swore off. It was the same old Hollywood mumbo jumbo that he knew so well, except that it was being done under a copper sun and was supposed to be an oil-well picture shot in the Middle East. But it was easier to use the local camels and rig the Andalusians up in burnooses, which made some sense. The gypsies were all Moors, anyhow; the camels came from a nearby game preserve; the mock-up oil rig was convincing; and there was always the Spanish army for extras. The noise was the same. Take and retake and retake — the same smack of the take slate, the same harassed script girl, the same ill-tempered director, and the same distractive cough into the sound track. Once in a while an aircraft would zoom low and wreck the take, or a Jeep would get mixed up with the camels; but then, that was picture-making anywhere: a bloody dull way to make a living, Alec thought dourly, as he announced that in future he would sleep late of mornings, to prepare himself for the flamenco ordeal of nights, and possibly go sight-seeing in the afternoons. Barbara was amiable about the whole thing.

"I do quite understand, sweetie," she said. "It must be terribly dull for you, just standing around while we do the close-ups and matching shots and middle shots and long shots and insurance shots and all the rest of this vital trivia.

But I have some happy news for you. The weekend's free: Svengali over there has wrapped up my sequence, and he's going to torture somebody else from Friday to Monday. We can do exactly what we want. Isn't that splendid?"

"It is, indeed. The trip can now be described as worth the effort. In light of that wonderful news, do you suppose we might give the clickers and clackers a little rest tonight, and perhaps flout the local customs by eating in our rooms and going to bed early?"

"Poor, poor Alec," Barbara said, and smoothed his hair. "How you do suffer."

"I don't mind some aspects of it," Alec said. "But it's enough to sit up all night with a bunch of gypsies without being sneered at all day by a bunch of camels."

They strolled the streets, buying things — Alec bought some gorgeous evil-smelling carved-leather chaps he didn't need, and a wicked-looking hunting knife he didn't need, and was measured for some boots he didn't need, and fought off the inclination to buy some *trajes cortos* he certainly didn't need.

"But you'd look wonderful in them," Barbara said. "I've got some to wear to the *tientas* —" She clapped a hand to her mouth. "I forgot, clean forgot. We're invited out to Juan Mendoza's *finca* — *ganadería*, actually — for Sunday's *tienta*. A *ganadería* is a bull-raising ranch, and a *tienta* is —"

Alec tweaked her nose.

"I know what is a *ganadería*. And a *tienta* is where they test the young cows for bravery, because the fighting spirit of the breed comes from the mother's side. I'm the bull expert in this family, remember? You've sure gone real flamenco for a girl who's only been in Spain for a couple of weeks. Why don't you try talking to me in English? I understand that, too."

"My boy Alec Barr, the supercilious son of a bitch, is back," Barbara said without rancor. "Why do you always try to steal my toys?"

Alec shook his head.

"I don't want to steal your toys. But I am a little amused at how thoroughly ladies become Hispanofied after two weeks in the bull country, or Italianated when they've been seven days in Rome and spent a dirty weekend in Capri."

"Do you want to go to this calf testing or not?" asked Barbara. "It's fun, I'm told. Big fiesta — lots of pretty people and big booze and fine food."

"Sure." Alec smiled at the childish excitement in her eyes. "I haven't been to one in ages. Not since Mexico with Tom Lea."

They sat now at a café table and ordered *manzanilla* and *tapas* — prawns and olives and anchovies and fried octopus and ham and cheese.

"There's so much I haven't seen," Barbara said wistfully, chewing around a big prawn. "I suppose that's why I kind of show off when I run into something new. I haven't even seen a bullfight, let alone a *tienta*. Exactly what is the purpose, anyhow, apart from fun and games?"

"It's mostly an excuse to get drunk," Alec said. "A big house party. But the basic idea is, you test the two-year-old calves for bravery. You put the calves, male and female, up against a picador on a horse to see how many pics they'll take. The brave heifers, who keep charging the horse despite the pain of that iron pike, are set aside to be bred to the stud bulls. The nervous become veal for the market."

"How about the little boy bulls?"

"They get a shot at the pike, too. The difference is that while they cape the cows, for fun, after the picador bit, they don't cape the bull calves. They only give the little bulls three shots with the lances, because they don't want to discourage their hatred for men on horseback — men on horseback whom they will meet two years hence when they are playing for keeps and the little bull calf, having been adjudged brave, will go out into that nice arena to be rendered into steak. Possibly for the poor, or possibly to be sold in the butcher shops as *carne de toro* — bull's meat — instead of just plain old *carne*."

"It all sounds very intricate. How do you know that the courage passes through the mother?"

"I don't know it. I only know what I've been told. And Spain is a very intricate country. Where is this *ganadería?*"

"Not far. About thirty minutes outside of town. I forget the name of the place. But Juanillo is sending his car for us about noon Sunday, if it's all right with you."

"It's fine with me," Alec said. "How do you know this Juanillo?"

"Just around. He's nice. Met him with some people at a flamenco. He took me to dinner a couple of times."

"What did he do with his wife when he took you to dinner?"

"Wife?" Barbara's reaction was honestly blank.

"Wife. They all have wives. But I don't expect you'll meet her Sunday. Wives don't get asked to *tientas* as a rule. Only pretty *americanas* and *francesas* and *inglesas* — and other visiting firemen, like writers and movie actors — get asked to *tientas*. Spain is a very intricate country, like I said."

"He never mentioned any wife," Barbara said thoughtfully.

"He wouldn't. It's an old Arab habit that rubbed off after about eight centuries of Moorish occupation. This Andalusian country ain't Europe, sweetie pie. It's Africa. Europe stops at the Pyrenees. A lot of people still don't realize that Spain is still Moorish. Anything that starts with *el* or *al,* from algebra to alfalfa to Alhambra, is Arabic. That nice dirty river is not really Guadalquivir. It's Vad-el-kebir, bastardized."

"You make me so damned mad sometimes," Barbara said, with no indication of anger. "You're a smart ass, you know that? You make me feel so stupid."

"I'm not a wishful smart ass," Alec said. "I'm a writer. Just like you're a ham. We're both hams. You adopt the protective coloration of a country or a situation or a group just as a chameleon changes his color. Yours is surface — Smithfield ham. I soak up my contact with situation and store it away. That makes me a Serrano ham. I'm cured in the snows, after I've been cut off the pig, before I'm fit for consumption. But we're both hams, in the end. And I could as easily have said *al fin* or *au fond,* if I was swanking it up."

Barbara stuck out her tongue at him.

"Let's go back to the hotel and stop being smart asses," she said. "I don't want any lunch. These *tapas* are too much. What I want is a nap in a cool, dark room."

"Your aim is noble, if not exactly in the mind," Alec said, and clapped his hands for the check.

A fat Jaguar was waiting in front of the hotel when Alec and Barbara came down. The whipcorded chauffeur touched his gap.

"*Buenos días, señorita,*" he said. "*Señor,*" as an afterthought to Alec. "Don Juan extends his compliments," he said in Spanish, "and regrets that he could not be here in person."

I'll bet a pretty, Alec thought, that even if the house is full of guests, that Don Juan would have found it possible to encounter the *señorita personalmente* if the word hadn't spread that the *señorita* had a Yankee boyfriend in town. I do love the Spaniards, particularly the Southern Spaniards. Everything from bathroom to breakfast to bed is *muy torero* — a pass with the eggs, *verónicas* with the bacon.

"Nice car," Alec said. "Must have cost a fortune to get it into the country." He patted the red-leather upholstery. "I'm only surprised it isn't a Mercedes or a Rolls."

"He keeps those for Franco," Barbara said. "Now you be nice and uncynical, and for Christ's sake, speak English. Juan is very proud of his English. Don't go hitting him with any Spanish slang, just to impress him because you're wearing a tweed coat instead of the *traje corto*. Snobbery gets you nowhere, even when it's inverse."

"Why," Alec said mildly, "I am only wearing tweeds because I don't have any *trajes cortos*. I do not intend to fight any cows today with the rest of the tourists. And speaking of *trajes cortos*, may I say you look very fetching in yours?"

She was, indeed, looking very sharp in the *ranchero*, the country costume. A flat gray *Cordobés* hat was tilted over the blonde hair, which she had twisted tight and swept up in a knot. The shirt collar was stiff and prim and almost little-girly. The narrow tie was black and proper over the frilled front of her shirt, and the bolero jacket was dove gray.

A black cummerbund confined the slim waist of her highly braced trousers, which were circumspectly striped with black on gray, in the manner of a banker's costume. They were short, split at the bottom, meeting her flat-heeled rawhide boots just below the calf.

"When did you order this outfit?" Alec asked.

"The second day I got here," she said. "You never know when some nice man will ask you to a *tienta*. I didn't want to accept the invitation wearing tweeds. Anyhow, Juanillo says he wants to teach me bullfighting, and you can't do it in a skirt."

"*¡Olé!* For the mother of La Virgen de la Macarena," Alec said, and reaped a response from the chauffeur. Alec concluded immediately that the chauffeur didn't care much for his presence.

The trip through the flat fields of wheat and rice was uninspiring, if dusty. Andalusia is only an extension of North Africa, and its hills like camels and long flats are equally uninspiring. Camel country, Alec thought. Camels and goats and bulls. Sun and rocks. Small trees and short water. Good bull country — make 'em walk over the rocks to water — and always an oasis in the middle.

The oasis was spectacular. A sudden island of greenery blurted at them as the chauffeur turned off the dusty main road into a dustier small winding road. He stopped the car to open a gate, drove the car through, and then got out to close the gate again. Black blobs of bulls appeared on the long sweeps of pasture. The excess of verdure came closer, and now the road was lined with flowers in huge pots — geraniums — and, as they neared the house, great beds of coxcombs with blossoms as large and solid as loaves of bread, as red as the insides of the pomegranates that grew from glossy green-leaved trees interspersed with the golden globes of oranges.

The *casa grande* was white plaster, strangled in red and purple bougainvillaea. It was classic Spanish-Moorish, sprawling over an expanse of watered green, red tiles; approachable through an archway, pillared and porticoed. A swimming pool winked blue-eyed to the left — trees shaded the big house. A vast patio surrounded the many doors, all cut in arches. White pigeons wheeled and carved small jet streams over the red roof tiles. The curving driveway was packed with Cadillacs and Jags and Bentleys and Mercedes-Benzes. There seemed to be a solid acre of roses, and another acre of orange and lemon and olive.

"Ya está," the chauffeur said, pulling up the Jaguar as if it were a horse. *"Creo que el dueño está en el otro patio. Es la hora de cokteles."*

Cheeky bastard, Alec thought. Even I know it's Martini time, bull ranch or no bull ranch. And the *dueño* is bound to be on the other patio, because that's where the shade is and it is exactly one P.M., Andalusian standard time.

"Gracias para sus bondades," Alec said as they got out. *"Donde está la ruta para los cokteles?"*

"Este lado," the chauffeur said, touching his cap. *"A sus ordenes, señorita."* Pause. *"Señor."*

"And what was all that?" Barbara asked.

"Nothing very much. I just thanked him, and asked him

which way was the booze. I've a feeling he disapproves of me. I ain't wearing country bullfight clothes, and I seem to be cutting in on the boss's girl friend."

"Now you just stop it," Barbara said. "Just stop it right now. Stop being cynical and superior. We're guests here, and you're an added starter."

"I know it," Alec said. "And I feel like an added starter. No matter. I'll be good and speak only English and perhaps maybe a little pidgin Spanish to show I'm a tourist. I wish I'd worn my *Cordobés* hat, except it clashes so with Irish tweeds, don't you think?"

"You —" Barbara stopped as a tall brown man came down the flagged, flower-hedged path to meet them, both hands outstretched.

"Barbara!" he said. "So very enchanted you could come and bring your friend." He took both her hands, then bowed and kissed her right hand, planting the kiss on his own thumb. He turned to Alec, bowed, and then extended his hand.

The grip was firm. The eyes were the blue-green of the South, clear in the baked brown face. The moustache was a charcoal line over the red lips, and the teeth were dazzling. The body was wearing a *traje corto,* but, as host, Juan Mendoza had allowed himself a red necktie. It went well with the ruffled shirt and the gray short jacket.

"Alec Barr, *a su disposición,*" Alec said, without thinking. *"Encantado, y muchisimas gracias para su bondad de incluirme."*

One finely drawn black eyebrow arched.

"It is your house," the owner said. "You speak Spanish well, Señor Barr. So few Americans do; it is always surprising. It is an honor to meet you, Mr. Barr. Barbara has told me so much about you. Tell me, *guapa*, how is the picture going?" He transferred his attention. "No, tell me later; first we must go and meet our other friends and have a drink and then you must tell me everything. This way, please, to where you can hear the noise."

Barbara cut her eyes dangerously at Alec as they walked toward where the noise was. You promised to be nice, the slitted eyes said. You promised to be nice and not be a smart ass about bulls or Spain or anything else.

Alec nodded, and they walked into a seething mass of people. A bar had been set up on the other patio, which was also flanked by big clay jars of geraniums and bordered in vast beds of wide-eyed pansies and the loaflike coxcombs, with roses crawling up the trees. This patio stood hard by the swimming pool, and the bar was sheltered with a kind of Polynesian thatched-roof hut of palm fronds and cane.

"First we get a drink, and then I introduce," the host said. "There are so many people and I am so bad at introduction. Some you know from the last party, Barbara — Pepe and Chelo and Teresa and Ramón and Ygnacio and Blanca and Abundio and Paco and Linda and Pilarín. The others are mostly *ingléses*. Maybe one or two from Madrid — an artist and a good writer of plays, I think, and two bullfighters taking a holiday. One is not bad. The other —" he shrugged. "But *simpático*. And what do you wish to drink?"

"Martini, please, with vodka," Barbara said. "If you have some?"

"Of course we have some. And you, sir?"

"I don't suppose you'd have a pink gin?" Alec could have kicked himself for being rude again, but something about

Don Juan's moustache and teeth annoyed him. His clothes fit too well, in any case.

"Of course we would have a pink gin. I went to school in England," said Don Juan. "Would you like to swirl the bitters yourself? Although Eladio here" — gesturing at the bartender — "is reasonably expert."

Touché, Alec thought. It takes one to know one. He inclined his head respectfully in the direction of the bartender. Again he spoke in Spanish, but at the bartender.

"I should be delighted," he said, using the subjunctive, "to place myself in the capable hands of your *peón de confianza.*"

"*Un* Martini with vodka, drry on the rrocks," the host said, "and *un* peenk geen, *à la inglésa.*"

Eladio the bartender smiled a tiny smile at Alec as he twirled the glass to spread the Angostura evenly. I don't think his bartender likes the son of a bitch either, Alec thought, and then thought again: Why do I think of him as a son of a bitch? Jealous of a man who has done me no harm, or just out of my depth with a lot of Spanish aristocracy? People who fight calves on Sunday for gags? People who never did a lick of work in their lives? Quit being a boy, boy. You've been through this before, in college.

Alec raised his glass.

"Health," he said, this time in English. "Chin-chin." He tasted his drink and raised the glass again at the bartender. "Perfectly constructed," he said in Spanish. "You must have an English grandmother."

The bartender's tiny smile split into a grin.

"*Irlandesa,*" he said. "Irish, *Señor.*"

"Now we go and see all the lovely people," Juan Mendoza said. He took Barbara by the elbow. "I don't think you have encountered my brother Tomás yet, nor my cousin Carolina."

There was nothing really wrong with it, Alec thought — nothing at all. But I never feel really in it. I know who I am and what I do. I know what I got and how I make it and who respects me for what I do and what I got. There are bulls' heads with no ears in this lovely cool adobe house with the black beams against the white plaster and the red flowers in the jugs. There are the moth-bitten heads of deer and the heads of ibex and the heads of pigs in the long hallways, and I got better tigers and lions and elephants and leopards. They call hunting the *caza grande* here, and feel like they've had a big day if they shoot some poor deer with a horn on his head. They get their rocks off by watching some beardless boy in tight pants kill a bull —thirty thousand people in a *plaza de toros* dying vicariously while a kid in a gold jacket and tight pants waves a red flag at a bull and accepts the possibility that he might lose his manhood. If he had any to lose, which is doubtful.

And now we are all gathered together over this interminable lunch — my God, *gazpacho, gambas, pollo, judias, filete, ensalada, patatas, pan, flan,* the whole bloody lot, with three kinds of wine in pottery mugs, before we get to the anisette — in order to work up another kind of appetite to go out to the private bull ring to watch a guy on a horse shove a lance into a calf. Then a bunch of drunks who should be having a siesta will get down into the ring and the host will take one end of a *capote* and the prettiest girl will take the other end and they will play bullfights with the calves.

"You know about the bulls?" The host was being polite. "You have seen some *corridas*, Mr. Barr?"

"A little. I've seen some few *corridas*."

"Do you like them?"

"Very much. When the man doesn't ruin the bull. And the horns aren't shaved. And not too much laxative administered before the bull comes out of the *toril*." Now why did I say that? Alec asked himself.

Here came the arched eyebrow again.

"Whom have you seen?"

"The last Belmonte. Manolete. The early Arruza, Dominguin — Luis Miguel — after the war. The earliest Ordonez. I never knew his father, except as a manager. Niño de la Palma was a little ahead of me. So was Gaona. Some others I knew in Mexico. Like Silverio."

Olé for you, father of the show-offs.

"You have written perhaps about bulls?"

"No."

"But why? You seem to know about them."

"I can't stand the thing about the horses." Alec was making a feeble joke for the Englishwoman on his right.

The eyebrow again. No sense of humor here.

"But you know we pad them now?"

"That's just it." Oh, damn me, I can't help it, Alec thought. He's putting me on.

"The fact is that I hate horses, and when they stopped getting it in the guts, I kind of gave up the *afición* business. Also, when they started cutting the vocal cords so the tourists couldn't hear them scream, it put me off my stroke."

"*Ooooh.*" Small squeak from the British lunch partner.

Don Juan laughed a hearty host's laugh.

"For a moment I thought you were serious. Now I see you make a joke. We call it in Spanish a *'chiste inglés'* — English humor. Truly, why have you not written about the bulls?"

Alec shrugged. "Truly, everything worth writing about bulls has been written — Hemingway; Tom Lea; Barnaby Conrad; some woman, I forget who; a couple of Mexicans; at least a thousand Spaniards; and, finally, an American, a friend of mine named Rex Smith, who did a biography of all the bulls and bull people. It seems to me the subject has been tapped out — exhausted. Bulls have now become a property for the tourists."

Don Juan Mendoza, the host, was leaning on the lance now, burling it. "The bulls don't move you anymore, then?"

"No. They don't move me anymore. Neither do the bullfighters. Not since Manolete."

"And Manolete moved you. Why?"

"Because both the man and the bulls were honest. The man worked his *corrida* day by day, without looking to the winter bookings in Mexico or Venezuela. And the bulls had strong legs and unclipped horns."

"You have been to *tientas* before, Mr. Barr?"

"Several. Many." Here it comes again. Up goes the eyebrow.

"Have you ever tested the calves? Have you ever known what it feels like to be in a ring with a wild animal — even a two-year-old calf?"

Alec shook his head and lit a cigarette.

"No, sir."

"Would you like to try your hand with the cape this afternoon? We could easily arrange a more suitable costume."

Alec shook his head. "No, sir. I'm basically frightened of cows. I got butted once when I was a kid."

The table exploded in laughter, with three exceptions — Alec, the host, and Barbara Bayne.

Alec turned to his British neighbor. "I didn't really mean that about the horses," he said. "I love horses, really. I've often hunted with them."

"Oh?" the squeaky voice asked, restored to faith. "Foxes? Wild boar?"

"No." Alec raised his voice a little. "When I hunt from horseback, it's mostly African elephant and, once in a while, lion."

That'll hold the bastard, he thought, and attacked his *flan*. The host was not yet finished.

"You hunt elephant and lion from horseback?"

"Yes. And sometimes rhino."

"But you are afraid of cows?"

"Exactly. I understand elephant and lion and rhino. I do not find myself fascinated by cows. A twelve-inch horn up your backside is just as long as the best horn on a four-year-old Miura. The prospect fails to amuse me."

"But elephants move you." This came as a statement.

Alec laughed.

"Often. I have probably run from more elephant than Gallo ever ran from bulls. Except when you deal with elephant you have no servant of confidence to take the elephant off you with a cape, and no *callejon* to jump over. I generally use big trees to hide behind."

Again laughter, with the exception of the three.

"It is a pity," the host said. "I would like to see a man who hunts elephant from horseback throw a cape at one of my calves."

"Sorry to disappoint you, Don Juan," Alec said. "But I am basically an *aficionado* of the spectator sports. I will sit, with your permission, in the judge's box, and drink brandy and award ears for the best performance."

"I think we will have coffee on the patio," the host said, and stood up. Barbara Bayne fixed Alec Barr with a look that might have served to define him as socially unacceptable.

Alec Barr sat lonely in the owner's seats of the private bull ring. Nearly everyone had had a crack at the calves. The two professional bullfighters — one fair, one nothing — had performed some flashy capework in taking the two-year-old heifers away from the man on the horse. The host, Don Juan, had strapped on his leather chaps and had produced some more flashy capework in the *quites*, performing acceptable *reboleras* and *chicueliñas*, wrapping the cape around him in a flash of magenta and yellow. The brother, Tomás, was playing the part of picador, maneuvering the horses well, leaning stoutly on the lance, laying the iron into the shoulders of the calves without unduly brutalizing them.

There are some damned good embryo bulls down there on that yellow sand, Alec thought, blinking against the slanting sun of the late afternoon, sitting off to himself in the white plaster of the little private ring. That last one took sixteen before she quit. She will be put to the seed bulls and yield some mighty calves for the brave festival.

I wonder, he thought, what makes me so bloody ornery? I

led that poor bastard Juan into a *cul-de-sac* at the lunch table. I was unforgivably rude. I guess it's merely insecurity in strange places, but I would love to see one of these big mouths with the amateur capes and the country clothes go up against a really nasty elephant in thick bush, or a leopard suddenly in the lap.

I got books to write, he thought. I got bills to pay. I don't need no horn up my ass. This business of the drunk social-ites playing with half-grown bulls is like playing chicken with cars, where the first one to swerve is a coward. You re-member that actress who got kicked in the face by a horse, in this same Spain, when she was learning how to bullfight from horseback? It took a lot of plastic surgery to get that dimple straightened out again, and she still does her close-ups from the left side of her face on account of the lip not turning up on the right side of her face when she smiles.

The hell with it, he said, and took a sip of the brandy. Now we got the star turn. Little Miss Twitchett, the Barbara-Bah-een from Hollywood, is going to fight a bull. *"Que tengas suerte,"* he whispered. That you should have luck.

Barbara looked marvelous out there on the golden sands of the arena. (Golden sands of the arena? What kind of writ-ing is that? *Arena* means "sand" in Spanish, unless you are in Cataluña, where it's spelled *arenys*. Smart ass.)

She had her *Cordobés sombrero* tipped at exactly the right angle, a little forward. Her backside was tight and trim in the striped pants. Her shoulders were braced well back, and those fantastic breasts pushed the frilled shirt forward, with the vest-cut jacket swinging free as she raised the cape to cite the little cow. (Little cow? Enough horns there to unzip her from navel to neck.)

"*¡Olé Barbarà! ¡Olé la señorita americana! ¡Olé la actriz brava!*" The voices swelled, all twenty of them, as Barbara planted her feet, one-two, as brave as Manolete who is dead, and cited the calf. (Barbara had the actor's gift of magnificent mimicry. At the moment she was playing *Blood and Sand* — second version, Tyrone Power — with himself, Alec Barr, playing critic by courtesy of the late Laird Cregar.)

"*Huh! Huh! Huh! Oh, hey, toro!*" He heard that trained actress voice saying the words just like something out of Hemingway. "*Eh hah! Hohohoho Hah! Toro!*"

Perfect take. Cut!

Now here came the brave cow. (Horns a good fourteen inches long and sharp as needles. Weight four hundred pounds and full of iron.)

Barbara (Belmonte) Bayne swung the cape with nice slow gypsy wrists, taking the cape low, sculpturing, head bowed, looking at the feet, as the calf came roaring, blood from the lancing streaming thickly from its shoulder. *¡Ay, qué torera!*

The calf passed her and took the cape with her as she went. Then the calf shook the cape irritably from the horn and looked again for an enemy. She found the enemy. It was wearing a beautifully cut *traje corto* — tight pants, fine bolero jacket, correct *Cordobés* hat, bosoms swelling under frilled shirt. Standing alone and uncertain.

"*Huh!*" This time it was the calf who cited, and charged. The host and his brother ran into the ring with capes, but not soon enough. Barbara ran for the *burladero*, the jokemaker, the little pantry in which bullfighters sometimes find it necessary to hide — with the calf goosing her all the way.

Barbara tripped and fell just as she achieved the entrance

to the *burladero*. The cow lowered her head (she's left-handed, bad left hook, Alec noted) and unzipped Barbara's tight pants as she crawled to safety behind the *burladero*.

The host and his brother caped the calf away, and Barbara emerged from the *burladero*.

Her backside shone white in the Sevillian sun. She had lost her hat. Her pants were down around her ankles. She had badly torn the front of her blouse and her nose was scraped by sand. Her face was ashen and she had begun to cry.

The host, Juan, ran up and wrapped her in a fighting cape.

Alec shuddered. He decided, if somebody could find her a pair of pants or something fairly decent to wear until she got back to the hotel, that this was going to be no night to spend on a late dinner, with flamenco until dawn.

"It is not," he muttered, "the hasty ascent up the thorn tree when you are being chased by a rhino that hurts so much. It is that long trip down." It was going to be a long trip back to the hotel, and a smart man would be well advised to keep his mouth shut.

Libby—The Girl Back Home

The office was unlike anything ever seen in Kensington, North Carolina. It had a rough stone-fronted wood-burning fireplace, and there was a white circular divan in front of it. It had a small blond wood bar in one corner, a bar that housed a small refrigerator. A flat glass dish containing Michaelmas daisies stood on the bar top. There was another vase of yellow roses on the corner of the boss's enormous desk. A low round coffee table stood in the center of the room in front of the divan, and bright green-and-red-chintz drapes rustled against one enormous window, which gave a close-up view of a very large weeping-willow tree. One wall, next to the fireplace, was lined with books, mostly in bright jackets, and if you stepped down two steps you entered a smaller office, where a smaller desk, blond wood filing cabinets built into the wall, and one easy chair with smaller coffee table chaperoned a typewriter and two telephones. There were flowers on the smaller coffee table as well, and the telephones were painted white. Both rooms were carpeted wall-to-wall. The carpet in the big office was apple-green, and the carpet in the smaller office was honey-blond. Private bathrooms adjoined both offices. The boss's bathroom contained a shower.

The offices had cost one hell of a lot of money. They had taken two months to do, and were spoken of as a scandal in the mill. Looks like a goddam bedroom, some said, not an office. Looks like a whorehouse, others said. Who ever seen an office with a chandelier?

Craig Price picked up Libby in the new Cadillac to take her to her first day of work. As they entered the door, which said PRESIDENT in tiny gold letters against the dark walnut, Craig suddenly, impulsively, caught Libby up in his arms and carried her across the threshold. He plumped her to her feet with a thud, and kissed her on the forehead. He swept one arm to cover both rooms in one grandiose gesture.

"Welcome," he said. "Your new home. I hope you like it."

Libby granted the room only a scanty glance, and looked deeply into Craig's eyes.

"It's lovely," she said. "I can't believe this is all coming true."

"I wish you were a bride instead of a secretary." Craig spoke almost to himself, knowing when he said it that it was only a matter of where and when.

"I like your new office," Maybelle Price said. "I'm surprised you don't leave the house and go live in it. Especially with all the modern conveniences and your fancy new redheaded secretary. You didn't waste much time, did you, boy? She qualifies on the tits real good. That's a real dish you got there. This makes it a real pleasure to be delayed at the office. Can she type? Or is that necessary?"

Craig chose to ignore the heavy sarcasm.

"Don't you get any wrong ideas about me and Libby," Craig said. "Her brother's my new spinning foreman, and he'll kill the man that lays a hand on her. It's just that she's smart as well as pretty, and I can't see any reason for having ugly old people to work with you or ugly old places to work in. There seems to be some sort of general idea that all offices should be ugly, and all secretaries should be chinless old maids. I happen to think different."

"I know," Maybelle said. "And you're the new president, so you're allowed to think different. But did you *have* to have two new bathrooms?"

"I didn't *have* to have the two new bathrooms. I *wanted*

two new bathrooms. I don't like the idea of going to the bathroom that my secretary's just left."

"She couldn't use the one the other help uses, I suppose? She'd be too grand for that?" Maybelle's voice was elaborately sarcastic.

"Look," Craig said. "Please don't make me mad. Leave Libby alone. This kid never had an inside bathroom before. We can take the cost out of my salary, or charge her a nickel every time she pees, if it bothers you."

"How was she fixed for flowers before?" Maybelle's voice flickered viperously at him. "You're going to wind up with a real tidy bill for flowers here if this gets to be a daily habit. Do you have to have flowers and a special toilet to make shirts that shrink?"

"As a matter of fact," Craig said, "I do. Perhaps some other people don't. I do. And they *don't* shrink."

"You've come a long way from the hungry sailor, haven't you?" Maybelle purred now. "Boy-oh-boy. Did you have a special toilet when you were going to sea on the *Wardance*? Did the bosun put flowers on the mess table?"

"No." Craig's voice flattened. "That's why I have to have a special toilet now. And flowers. And a Cadillac. And good clothes and a nice place to work. Just because I had to bathe and go to the toilet with eight other people and the bosun *didn't* put flowers on the table. I knocked cockroaches out of the biscuits. I had to eat and sleep with people I didn't like, and most of them were ugly. Would you like to shut up about this now and consider it the price of being married to a man with the same name?"

"I'll shut up," Maybelle said, "as long as your fancy ideas

don't eat too deep into the profits, or you may kind of find yourself without that power of attorney. And I wouldn't work too late at the office too often if I were you. You know how the help talks. You wouldn't like it back at sea, going to the john with eight other people, and no flowers on the table."

So she gives the sea business right back to me, and the trouble is, Craig thought bitterly, she's right. Like all women, she can smell what isn't actually there before it happens, because she knows someday it'll be there. I'd a hell of a sight rather be working late at the office with Libby than staying home with Maybelle — and Maybelle already knows it before I've even had a chance to prove it.

Working with Libby Forney was a delightful habit. Just looking at Libby was a delightful habit, and habit was all you could call it. Craig found it awfully easy to leave his breakfast table five minutes earlier in order to pick her up at her house. He found it just as easy to time his work-finish so that he could drop her off before he went home for supper. This became increasingly easy since he had incorporated the small icebox in his bar and obviated the necessity of going home for lunch at all. Libby kept the icebox stuffed with cheeses and fruit and the makings for sandwiches. It was easy to send out for coffee until Craig decided to put a hot plate in the corner and install an electric percolator, so that now lunch could consist of hamburgers and hot soup and decent coffee instead of the soppy stained cardboard cartons from the Greek. Lunch grew into a small ceremony, a happy time of the day, when all the hands were off on the lunch hour, the phone was still, and there was no noise in the plant. The implicit peace of that hour was almost profound. Craig would say:

"Hey, girl! Drop that typewriter and come make your boss a Martini. We've worked hard enough for right now."

Libby would hood her eyes demurely, and bat her lashes in the best-approved Southern fashion.

"You know I don't approve of drinking during working hours," she would say. "It's bad for the morale of the help."

"Oh, hell," Craig would say. "Unbend, relax. A little Martini never done nobody no harm. What are we having for lunch?"

"Bologna sandwiches, or some of that canned crab you bought the other day. Or cheeseburgers."

"Settle for the crabs. Won't be the first time, either. By God, girl, you make a fine Martini. Lookin' at you, sweetie".

"Lookin' at you, boss," with her small smile.

A tiny bow, each to the other, and then Libby would bustle about the icebox, put something on the hot plate, make the coffee, and Craig would think: *This is better than being married. This is almost like being in love, without all the trouble. It's like a picnic every day.*

He looked at the girl.

She was wearing a black linen suit and a simple white shirtwaist. There was nothing obvious to detract from the mahogany roan of her hair, which she had taken to wearing off her neck, high-piled on her head. She used no cosmetics except lipstick. She kept her fingernails short and uncolored. She was, Craig thought, the most ornamental piece of furniture in the office, or possibly in the world.

"Anybody ever tell you how very, very pretty you are?" he asked.

"Sure." She flashed a smile. "You. You always do. Every morning when you pick me up, and every day about this time, and every night when we have the one toddy before you take me home."

Craig slapped himself slightly on the head. "I must be losing my memory," he said. "I thought this was the first time I ever said it."

"You said it the first time you ever saw me, when I was a little girl," Libby said.

"So I did, so I did, and I was right. Except you came along fine like a good garden. You get prettier all the time and I don't know how I can stand it if it keeps ups. Not working with it all day long?"

"You fired Miss Mildred," Libby said. "Maybe I'll be next when I'm old and ugly. Have some of the cold crab and quit talking about me. It makes me nervous."

Craig had thought, when he carried his new secretary over the threshold of his new office, that it was only a matter of where and when. He had thought the same thing, really, that first day he ever saw her when he went to the Forney house for beer and sandwiches before they went fishing. He knew it, knew it surely, the night of his first new car, when he took her riding before he even showed the car to Maybelle. He believed that Libby knew it, and that her brother Red knew it, inevitably, but damned if he was going to do anything to spoil this beautiful kid who wasn't a kid anymore, but a glowing woman as ripe as a blush peach for the plucking.

Libby was now a creature of temptation to touch. Every

time she brought him a batch of correspondence or fixed him a drink or merely crossed his field of vision, there was a temptation to fondle her flank or lightly touch her shoulder, as innocently as one drops his hands to the head of a beloved dog or unthinkingly strokes the cat or even rubs the shabby spine of a favorite book or gently enjoys the mirrored sheen of a good piano. Or, on the other hand, as uninnocently as one unhooks a bra.

Libby was a flower, just unfolding its dewy petals in a joyous morning sun, and Craig wanted to smell it and see it and touch it, but something in him recoiled from the actual cutting of its stem. That the stemming was inevitable, he knew. This he found vastly puzzling to himself, because it had nothing to do with his marriage, nothing to do with infidelity, nothing to do with Libby's brother's fiercely protective attitude. It was almost as if he was trying to shield himself, to shore up and preserve one last shred of his boyish — would *niceness* be the word? he asked himself.

Craig's almost virginal physical avoidance of Libby persisted for a year.

It would be difficult for either Craig or Libby to say how or why they had suddenly commenced kissing. It had been like something Druid-sent from the forests, some tiny secret sign, some small smell, some slight, unplanned, musky indication of need to each other. Perhaps it had been the fresh flowers in the bowl, perhaps the intrusive breeze that stirred the curtains and let the sun-bright glow bow unbidden into gray-faced business. Or even perhaps the way Libby's skirt rustled when she brought in a tray of stolid correspondence, or the crispness of her shirtwaist, the liquid swing of her hips, or the shape of her small neat ears. Perhaps a birdsong, faintly heard, perhaps the memory of a good breakfast, perhaps the cheerful clanging of the mill machinery as it spelled harsh profit.

Libby placed the tray of correspondence on Craig's desk, and he could see the curve of her breasts as they fell forward from her body when she leaned over the desk. Suddenly he was out of his seat, kissing her, holding her close, with both their bodies blended, straining toward each other. Then Libby pushed him suddenly away.

"No! No, Craig! Not here. Even in the yard. Even in the street. Anywhere else but here or in our house."

Craig looked honestly surprised. He looked at the closed door, a door that could be locked against intrusion.

"Why not here? Why, of all places on earth, not here? We live here. It's our home." Craig shook his head. Women, my God, women.

"That's it, Craig. That's just it. We have to live here. And work here. And it's not — *ours*. Craig. I love you, Craig. But this is a good part Maybelle's and her family's. But it's not ours to make love in. And my brother works in the back of the mill. It's like having him in the same room with us. No, Craig."

Craig looked baffled, and more than a little hurt. She had kissed him as fiercely as he had wanted her ever since the first day he had seen her.

"Where, then? Where do you go to love somebody you love?"

"Not our house, either. That's Red's — *Red's*. Actually Red's. Not yours and mine. You can have me when you want me, but it has to be some place that's ours. I don't care if it's a sand dune or the back of your car or even a hotel room. But not here, and not there."

Craig frowned.

"I need a drink, girl," he said. "A stiff one. Suppose you do me a little bourbon and branch, while I collect my scattered brains. You had much practice kissin' fellows? That one was about two-hundred proof."

Libby smiled as she walked over to the liquor cabinet.

"I never had no practice a-tall kissin' fellows like that before. But I think it could shore git to be a habit."

"All right," Craig said. "We don't need the hillbilly dialogue just because I'm nervous. Don't feel you have to put me at ease just because we suddenly attacked each other. And we did, didn't we? Attack each other? Ferociously, I mean?"

"I wouldn't say *you* attacked *me*." Libby matched his grin with more calculated lasciviousness than one would expect from a girl in her latest teens. "Let's just say that I been practicin' up so I could attack you. So when I attack I make it stick. You got a lot of lipstick on your mouth, boss."

"You practice real good," Craig said. "Thanks for the drink. I know I got lots of lipstick on my mouth. It tastes just dandy. You havin' a drink?"

"I don't think I need one," Libby said. "I'm too young to kiss the boss *and* have a drink on one and the same day."

"Seriously," Craig said. "Seriously, sugar." They drove along the beach road to the Old Fort. Libby was sitting very close to him, and he could feel the pressure of her breast on his arm, the warmth of her long thigh pressed close to his. "Seriously, it's a hell of a problem, and the way you put it, I didn't want to talk about it in the office. I want you more than I ever wanted anything, my girl, but it's got to be a halfway house and that I hate. I'm still married with all the complications you know about. In a town like this we can't go scampering in and out of hotels, such as they are. And there's something dirty about these motels that I don't want to rub off on us. You know — too many people there before. I don't seduce lightly, do I?"

Libby shivered slightly, and Craig could feel her tremble.

"Let's stop here so I can kiss you again," she said. "So I can get you back again. Right here. There's nobody around for miles."

The little fishing shack had a "For Rent" sign on it. It sat on a high sweeping dune overlooking the beach on which the heavily white-plumed rollers pounded. It had a little rickety, precarious flight of planked stairs leading from the small porch to the beach below. Sea oats surrounded the cottage's salt-grizzled shingles, and silver gulls screamed and braced their wings as they rode the stiff breeze.

"What a sad, lonely little house, all by itself, away from everybody," Libby said. "I know what this house feels like."

"All alone on this beach where nobody ever comes except to fish, and then only in the fall," Craig murmured, half to himself. "I always loved to fish. You know, darling child, I think I will take up fishing as a hobby. I've been working too hard lately."

He threw the car into gear, and Libby looked at him in surprise. He hadn't kissed her again.

"Where are we going now?" she asked. "You're driving so fast, Craig."

"To the hardware store," he said. "I have to buy some fishing tackle and some camping equipment, because I have just rented myself a fishing shack. I hadn't realized how much I missed fishing until that day I went with your brother, and that's not real fishing, that bent pin-and-worm stuff. I'm a surf caster at heart."

Craig left the office after lunch for three days. He had not kissed Libby again, but had stayed so stiffly aloof that she looked hurt.

"What will I say if anyone calls?" she asked, rather plaintively, on the third day.

"Just say I'm back in the plant and to leave a message. Or else I've gone across the river and will be back by six. I will be back by six." He blew her an airy kiss. "Look after the store, Pete."

Saturday morning Craig got up late and dressed in rough clothing. He produced a rod and reel, a tackle box, and a bait bucket from the hall closet.

"What's all this?" Maybelle asked. "You being a boy scout again?"

"Yes," Craig said. "I'm going fishing."

"Who with?"

"A couple of fellows from the office. I'll be back by dark."

"You want me to fix you a lunch?"

"Don't bother. We'll grab a sandwich somewhere. 'Bye."

"Don't be late. You know we got people coming."

Craig took down the "For Rent" sign and threw it into the sea oats. He produced a key and opened the door.

"Come here," he said gruffly, and this time, when he picked Libby up in his arms to carry her across the threshold, he did not set her down with a thump or kiss her on the forehead.

"I love our house," Libby said. "It's not a sad little house anymore. It's a very happy little house. And I am a very happy big girl."

"I reckon I might say I ain't real miserable," Craig said. "Here, woman, put on my coat and fix us a pot of coffee on our happy little stove. It won't be the last you'll fix, so you might as well get in practice."

"Yes, master," she said, and Craig looked at her naked as she slipped into his coat, looking a little silly in a man's coat. He wondered, almost sadly, if anything so beautiful would ever happen to him again. Pessimistically, he rather thought not.

"I think we should pass a law," he said as she moved over to the tiny stove. "I think it should be against the law for you to wear clothes. Ever again, even in the office. Except that coat of mine, of course. Enough of it slips aside so I can get an occasional glimpse of what's inside."

"Well, it isn't nice for girls to go to work naked," she said, and turned swiftly to fling herself on him. "Oh, Craig, tell me, tell me true, was I — was I *nice?* I don't know anything about these things. I didn't — I didn't disappoint you? I wasn't too — too *eager?* Too dumb? Too — shameless?"

"I have been drinking entirely too much coffee lately anyhow," Craig said, with his face buried in her tumbled hair.

"Let the coffee go and come back here where you belong. I'll answer all your questions ten years from now."

It was not a bad little house at that, Craig thought, watching Libby dress and wondering afresh at the beauty of the girl — wondering especially anew at the frankness, the eagerness, the honest, innocent passion of this former child, this new young woman who had come to vibrant life under his hands. That she was virgin he indisputably knew. Physically she had certainly been virgin, but in her heart, and surely in her head, she had not been virgin.

"Were you planning to ask me if I still loved you, now I've had my wicked will?" he asked, chuckling.

"Not at all," she said, doing something with her hair, standing frowning into a little wrinkled mirror. "I was expecting you to ask me do I love you, now I've had *my* wicked will. I believe I do." She turned from the mirror, and her eyes hurt him. "Oh, how very, very much I do, and I always will. Oh, Craig, I've thought and thought about how it would be — and never knew it would be anything like this — until I feel almost ashamed of myself. I feel wicked because I'm happy. Aren't girls supposed to cry and carry on and things like that? Should I cry and carry on to prove I'm a nice girl?"

"No, but seeing as you're still in your slip, you can take it off again and come back here. I never want to leave here, this funny house of ours, with its little tin stove and all the awful things I put in it this week, including this bed. You're going to have to do a lot of redecorating, my lovely woman."

"It was sweet of you to send flowers," Libby said. "Are you sure we ought to — again?"

"I'm sure we ought to — *again,*" Craig said.

"You're late," Maybelle said. "Did you catch a lot of fish?"

"No," Craig said. "A few little ones. I gave them to the fellows."

"I don't know why you still insist on minglin' with these mill hands," Maybelle said. "Now you're president and all. Was it that redheaded Forney fellow you're so fond of you made him foreman?"

"No," Craig said. "It was a couple of other fellows. Look, I'm tired. That surf was awful rough. I'd like to turn in early."

"Well, you can't. You know very well we've got the Millers and the Wrights comin' any minute for some drinks, and we're all supposed to go to the King Crab for dinner later. You better hurry and get dressed. Maybe you better have one drink first. You're lookin' awful peculiar."

"That's not a bad idea," Craig said. "Fix you one?"

"I already got one," Maybelle answered. "You go on up and shower some of the fish scales off you, and I'll fix you a stiff one and put it on your dresser."

"Thanks, sweetie," Craig said, and went up the stairs.

Our house, Libby thought as she got undressed to bathe. *Our* house belongs to Craig and me, a little gray-shingled house that stands on the edge of the beach down near the Fort. Our house has a kerosene stove for heat and a bed that really isn't big enough for two people. It has a little stove to cook on, and some oil lamps, and one table and two chairs and no running water except from the pump in the back. Our house has an Indian blanket for a rug and another on the bed. Our house has an outside toilet — just like *we* always used to have, she thought — and a tin coffeepot and a shelf where you put the pepper and salt and coffee and maybe a bottle of whiskey and a can of sardines. Our house has some flowers on the little oilskin-covered table. Dear Craig. He must have worked like a Trojan, cleaning that place up and buying sheets and blankets and the other stuff. And the flowers. He must have driven all the way down there this morning just so there would be some roses on the table.

Libby got into the tub, and let the hot water stroke her. Why is it I feel so *good,* she thought? Why don't I feel *bad?* I haven't had a wedding or even a real love affair. I've just been in bed all afternoon with a married man who right now is at home with his wife. He won't — he *couldn't* — go to bed with her, not after this afternoon! Her new thoughts shrieked in her head. She stifled the shrieks and then thought dully: But as long as he lives with her he'll have to go to bed with her. And he'll be going to bed with me — in the afternoon in that *ugly* little house. With the kerosene stove and the oil lamps and the Indian blanket for a rug. That *ugly* little house. Libby suddenly began to cry, and suddenly, down below where love had entered and changed her from a girl to a woman, she began to hurt. The physical hurt was there, as if she'd been riding a horse, but it hurt worse in her breast, worse in her head. Libby saw herself naked with hostile eyes as she dried herself, and when she got into a nightgown, she went into the kitchen and poured herself a stiff slug of bourbon. It was the first drink she had ever taken alone. Then she went to bed and buried her head under her pillow, but she could not get Maybelle out of the room. Maybelle was sitting right there on the side of the bed with her. It wasn't Craig who was spending her wedding night with her. It was Maybelle, Craig Price's wife. Or perhaps, if Libby had been older, she might have called it conscience.

Valerie—The Girl Who Will Never Come Back

Valerie Dunstan Dermott settled into her seat and buckled on the seat belt. She heard the solid chunk of the door slamming and saw with satisfaction that there was practically nobody on the plane. That was good — she'd be able to take out two arm rests and sleep all the way to Rome, with luck. She would have a couple of drinks and then take a pill.

She opened her bag and drew out a compact. Her eyes were still scratchy from the unshed tears, and her nose looked a trifle pink. She was sick at heart, but she was honestly relieved to be leaving Kenya again. This time it *was* final, as all her thoughts of Brian were final now. That was finished. They were both finished. But she had never felt really divorced from him before. Now she felt utterly and completely divorced.

She sighed as the huge, nearly empty plane trundled out toward the takeoff strip, jouncing slightly over the tarmac. Her instinct about leaving Kenya in 1953 had been right. If she had not left then she would certainly be leaving now —

as, she knew, so many people who had bravely stayed on would be leaving now, with the Government changing and the country coming inevitably into black hands. It was no longer a white man's country at all — no longer a place to live safely and happily with love and peace.

The plane was racing down the strip now, its jets blasting, and she gave another sharp, aching sigh of relief as the wheels came up with a bump and the jet began its climb. She unsnapped the safety belt, took off her jacket, and laid it folded on the seat beside her for the stewardess to take. She was off now, off and away — safely out of Kenya. She would never come home again, because home was no longer home, as Brian Dermott was no longer her husband, as Brian Dermott was no longer her man. She relaxed the seat control, crossed her legs, and let her mind travel backward as the jet hummed monotonously in the sky.

When Valerie Dunstan Dermott left Kenya at the height of Mau Mau emergency and went back to London to live, she had at first tried to explain to the people she met at parties that she had left a small and rather complicated war behind her in East Africa. The people she met at parties were quite sure of it; the most dreadful things were always happening out East, and it served Whitehall exactly right.

After a while Valerie stopped telling people that she had been born and raised in Kenya. She was weary of hearing people say, "Oh, how very interesting," and then making some polite remark about lions or a dimly recalled cousin who had been sent to the colonies for his sins, such people the while staring over her shoulder or down her dress, depending on the sex of her partner. So far as most of London was concerned, Africa stopped at Suez and did not recommence until it touched Johannesburg. There was some vague idea that the Congo was flung into the middle, but the Congo was teeming with Belgians and gorillas and was therefore hopeless on both accounts, even if you overlooked the climate, which was said to be shocking.

"Oh, and did you do all sorts of amusing things in Africa?" was another line that she heard frequently and which she finally learned to avoid, since she could never fully explain that Kenya was not entirely populated by dissolute younger sons and fugitives from early Evelyn Waugh fiction. She didn't have to be from Africa any longer — she looked Latin, she had attended school in England for ten years as a girl and young woman, and she was certainly pretty enough to stand on her own as that divine young Mrs. Dunstan-Dermott with the unbelievable eyes and hair. Neither the unbelievable eyes — which were slightly uptilted at the corners and an odd gypsy blue-green — or the unbelievable hair, which was sleekly black as a crow's wing in the sun — had become any less divine since Valerie had given up Kenya dust for London grit and rolling yellow fog. As she tended toward her thirties, she was quite frequently mistaken for a film star when she lunched at the Mirabelle or danced late at the Café de Paris.

Valerie Dunstan — she never really thought of herself as Valerie Dermott — was almost symptomatic of her times; typical of many upper-middle-class postwar marriages that had been granted no chance to jell, which had left few showing scars, and which were uncomplicated by either children or severe financial problems. When Valerie divorced Brian for desertion, in an uncontested action, he had quite decently settled two thousand pounds a year on her, which was ample money for a woman alone. She had not asked for the money, but he had volunteered it, and she had not been hesitant about accepting it.

With it she was able to live in what her friends called a jewel box of a small duplex flat in Hill Street, a flat with a very large, high-ceilinged pale green paneled living room, with two bedrooms upstairs and a commodious modern kitchen off the hall. It had a tiny terrace behind, window boxes in front, and cost her five hundred pounds a year in rent and rates. She furnished it in Chinese modern and had sent out to Kenya for a few exotic touches — a sprinkling of African ebony heads and some leopard and zebra skins that she had sewn into poufs for scattering on the dead-black rug of her living room. Her fireplace burned wood, and she owned a good TV and an excellent collection of recordings for her hi-fi.

Valerie loved her flat. She was just a stone's throw off Grosvenor and Berkeley Squares — she was no distance at all from the Mirabelle and Les Ambassadeurs, from Siegi's and the White Elephant, from all the amenities of Shepherd's Market and Curzon Street and, of course, a sound pub like the Red Lion. There was the handiness of the Dorchester Hotel, and the quiet elegance of the little Bon Viveur Club for girl lunches. There was nothing lacking in the Curzon Street area — taxi ranks, news vendor, bank, cinema theaters, butcher, chemist, vintner, greengrocer, florist, tobacconist — a short stroll took her to everything she needed. Her daily came three hours for six days a week and kept the flat spotless. She knew no neighbors to speak to, passed no porters, and was able to live her life without encouraging any gossip whatsoever. She planted geraniums in her window boxes and tossed together small chop-and-salad meals when she had no feeding invitations. She went to the pictures and to the theater, read a great deal, watched the TV and played her records. The flat was just precisely large enough to hold an occasional cocktail party or Sunday brunch or buffet, but never capacious enough to trap her into extensive entertaining. Valerie drank moderately, but she kept her little bar well stocked for the friends who dropped in before the theater or sometimes for a nightcap after an evening out.

She was a strikingly beautiful woman now, tall with lovely long legs and pale petal skin and a figure that let her eat anything. She dressed simply in beiges and blues and blacks, which did extra things for the opalescent eyes and shining hair, and she looked divine in slacks and shorts, in ski pants and jodhpurs. She received more than ample opportunity to show off her body in these figure-testing costumes, because she swam, skied, and rode well, and was forever being asked out to people's houses on country weekends. She had sufficient money to travel decently abroad when the mood struck her, and so went regularly to the South of France, occasionally to Italy and Spain, and usually to Switzerland — to Gstaad or St. Moritz — at least once during the winter. As often as not she was an all-expense invited guest, because Valerie Dunstan was a cheery, handsome person who held her liquor well and so far had kept aloof from being cited in any messy divorce actions. If she slept around she slept around quietly and in good taste, or so everyone said. She had, most people said, fixed up her life a proper treat.

Valerie had hated England when she left it after finishing

her schooling — and two reasonably shattering love affairs — to go back to Kenya and marry Brian Dermott in 1952. But a short time in Kenya as the wife of Brian Dermott had healed her of colonialism, in much the same sense that the young American naval type had set her dead against uniforms. She had not been prepared for Kenya in its most modern interpretation — she had gone home in 1952 expecting to resume life in a green and pleasant land; expecting certainly to marry and grow suitably plump among dogs and polo ponies and lively Sunday chatter at The Brown Trout or some other comfortable pub; to rear her children strong and ruddy and handsome on a well-remembered farm in easy view of Mount Kenya; to raise them *not* to be drunks and pansies and useless, languid lechers.

She had not gone to Kenya expecting to have her easy prospects shattered by a sudden racial tumult that took her almost from a honeymoon bed to the stewardship of a good portion of her husband's ruined family. She had not been prepared to become mistress of a household where the chatelaine wore a pistol as well as a bunch of keys, where you locked away the servants in a compound every day at sundown for their protection as well as your own; she was not prepared for a life in which every creak of floorboard made you flinch with shrieking nerves and every crunching footfall outside might foretell an enemy.

Valerie had wanted a family of her own, as soon as ever she and Brian could start one. She had found her family sooner than she expected: her husband's old foster mother suddenly widowed of the tough little man she had leaned on; her husband's sister, terribly burned in the raid that killed her foster father horribly — and finally, her husband's fatherless younger brother, a quiet, shy boy who wore a pistol with as much assurance as did his big brother Brian, her stranger-husband.

Valerie had wanted a tame husband of her own, to love and be loved by in the spanking new wing he had built for her onto the family home. Instead she had lost her husband to the black forests where he had gone to hunt men. He had come home occasionally, bloody-handed and heartsick, filthy dirty and usually very drunk from the things he had been doing, which caused him to grind his teeth horribly at night and sweat the bedclothes in his nightmares. It had got worse as time went on and the tension mounted; she and Brian no longer made love because whatever Brian was doing up the mountain had stolen his demonstrable manhood, and sex became a grim pageant of nail-biting frustration on her part until her husband became frighteningly resigned to not touching her any more.

It was a pity, Valerie often thought, that she had not been built of the properly corny pioneer stuff like her sister-in-law Eleanor, who had survived it all — had even taken on the black orphan of one of the very Kikuyu gangsters who had killed her foster father, and who finally had evidently repaired her heart as well as she had fixed her fire-scarred face. Nell Dermott was married now to a British doctor, George Locke, and they had both seemed terribly happy when they came to London and called on her with news of home and Brian during the time that Nell was having her burned face redone by the Harley Street plastic surgeons. It was a pity that there were no Harley Street plastic surgeons to repair the kind of injuries that *she* had received at the hands of Kenya and its people, Valerie sometimes thought, when she was feeling lost and lonely on a dreary, fog-palled London Sunday.

It was not her fault that she was not shaped to the Nell Dermott mold, Valerie thought. She was not meant to be heroic; being locked into the bathroom by your husband — before you gave up that sort of thing entirely — while you made sure you wouldn't have any babies, was not her idea of utter connubial bliss. She was not brave; she hated living penned up in a land where limitless space was supposed to be as much a part of your life as the furniture; she hated the endless drudgery of housework in a country that was famed for the number and cheapness of its black servants; she loathed the atmosphere of fear and suspicion, the distrust of everything black, even old servants like Brian's Juma — and above everything else, she had none of the old settler's abidingly stubborn passion for the land. It was true that Valerie Dunstan had been born in Kenya, but her people had come to Africa as young marrieds, and had died before the second war, a long time before the going got sticky.

She had wept, of course, when she and Brian parted after that horrid scene in Nairobi. It had all been innocent to the extreme — she was young, and bored blue with being cooped up on that lonely farm with death creeping about in the house as well as outside. She had never really been married, and she was already sick of being married and having no husband at home to make her know she was married.

The emergency in Kenya was just like another war, with the husbands all away. The women were desperately nervous and angry at the disruption of their lives, and there were thousands of lonely, attractive men among the British troops they kept sending out. She was young and she was healthy and beautiful and she liked men physically, and sooner or later she would have been playing the old game that had made Kenya famous for infidelity for fifty years. A great many of them had played the game with eager zest — Nairobi had become suddenly very gay behind the tears.

Well, it hadn't come to that. The lost baby had fixed that. Brian had returned to the forests and she had nipped smartly back to England. Perhaps if she hadn't lost the baby she might have stayed, but . . . well. The baby had never got more than started, and that was that. And this fresh-come time she had loved England, if only for being so different from Nairobi.

Once, lonely as a girl in school, she had yearned for the violent beauty of Kenya, the infinite landscapes, the blue, cruel escarpments, the long green hills, and the wind-rippled seas of golden grasses. She had mourned the bracing nip of evening air in the White Highlands, the feeling of still-untasted freedom, the frightening grandeur of the great dark forests of the Aberdare, and the close-touching communion with the wild things; the zebras grazing alongside cattle and the occasional lion sitting like a big dog by the side of the road. She had remembered nostalgically the shabby spaciousness of the homely Kenya farmhouses, and the kind of roughly expansive living that made no special fuss about driving a hundred miles over vile roads for drinks with a friend — she had romanticized the living that had left all doors unlocked and had been deeply shocked on her return to find that now all doors were closed, all windows barred.

Now she loved England for all the things that Kenya had

cheated her of; for the tender sweetness of its gentle countryside, its winding shaded roads fluffed with the dainty white
blossoms of haw and the showery yellow exuberance of for-
sythia. She loved the soft rains and even the pressing fogs
that shut one in and made an island of a room; the weath-
ered old gray buildings and the bustling traffic and the great
stalls of flowers and fruits; the theaters and the lights of Piccadilly and the Strand and the clubs and restaurants of May-
fair; she adored all the entrancing shops with their solid,
comforting clutter of silver and leather and woolens. But
most of all she luxuriated in the *security* of London — the
bobby standing pink-faced and trustworthy on the corner;
the busbied guard changing station, in front of the palace;
the almost never-failing courtesy and humor of the cabbies
and liftmen; even the imaginative Cockney curses from the
barrow boys, and the pigeon-droppings coppery-green on
the old statues, steeped her in a warm feeling of safety and
well-being. Perhaps she would marry again someday, if she
found someone who wouldn't bore her, and she could risk
losing the alimony. She did not think of herself as likely to
fall madly in love again — after this last three months, she
doubted if she had ever been solidly in love with Brian. He
had been very handsome, it was true, and he was very romantic at a time when white hunters had momentarily re-
placed jet pilots and movie actors as glamorous figures. But
love him? She didn't even know that they would have
worked out well in bed, over the long haul, after the first
frenzied attraction of two young and beautiful healthy
bodies for each other. Certainly this last three months of bed
hadn't been anything shining or special. She didn't know if
there was anything actually *in* Brian, under the physical

strength and charm and good looks — any more, she was forced to admit in honesty, than she knew if there was anything actually in *her*.

Valerie Dunstan, sitting in the air-cooled loneliness of the jet, told herself cruelly now that she was a vegetable, a healthy, beautiful, reasonably happy vegetable. She had no particular scruples about letting the occasional attractive man into her bed if he seemed to want it badly enough. She enjoyed it, as a rule, and she could always find it by crooking a finger, and dismiss it if it got irksome. What she wanted was no real entanglements with heartbreak and misery and, most of all, discomfort and uncertainty, at the end of it. She had left her first real love with the American naval gentleman; she had left her illusions about marital security by a burned-out barn on a long green hill in the White Highlands of Kenya in British East Africa.

Now the plane's loudspeaker system was informing the passengers that the peak of Mount Kenya could be seen to the left. She decided she did not want to see The Mountain, and buried her face in her hands. What she wanted to see again was the little flat in Hill Street. In London, which, forever more, was home.

Penny—The Nymphette

Spinning down the highway with the top down — it was still warm enough in the early afternoon — and two pretty women snuggled in the broad red-leather front seat beside him, Alec was conscious of a feeling of intense well-being. He was going home, and he was going home to work. The nagging conscience was eased, and the lush lunch was still warm in his stomach.

The women were silent, listening to the *whish* of the tires and to the radio playing softly from WPAT in Paterson.

"Penny," Di Lawrence said suddenly.

"Yes, Ma?" Penny's voice was sleepy.

"Not you, baby. I was offering Mr. Barr your namesake for his thoughts. What's on that keen authorial mind, Alec, this bright autumnal afternoon?"

"Nothing. Everything. I was just ruminating. College. Youth. Uncertainty. How fast it all moves. Mainly I was wondering when Luke gets back. I wired him this morning."

"Who's Luke?" Penny's voice was fully awake now.

"Luke? He's the other half of my hermitage. Luke is Luca Germani, ex-chief yeoman, USNR, second-generation Italian, hero of a thousand battles with Navy red tape, and for a long time the man who brings some semblance of order into my working existence. Luke runs my life when I am out here in Jersey, and he runs Jersey when I am off to the wars of Manhattan, Africa, or darkest Elsewhere. In short, Luke is my chief cook-and-bottlewasher-*cum*-secretary-foreman-slave."

"Explain. I don't think I ever heard you mention him before." This was Dinah.

"Not much to explain. Luke and I were in the Great War together. He was attached to my admiral's staff, and he was sort of allocated to me as personal secretary in charge of such heroic things as filing, cutting orders, fouling up personnel records. Skinny Wop — smart as hell — do anything you needed doing in the office. Made fine coffee. I didn't hear from him until well after the war, about the time I built the house in Jersey. It was like some sort of miracle. I had scarcely moved in and was having a lot of domestic trouble — the town servants hated moving back and forth, and there's not a lot of help forthcoming from the local Jackson whites; I needed my gal secretary in town, and Amelia loathed the idea of the hearty outdoor life on a Jersey lake. She also hated cooking.

"Well, I got a letter from Luke saying he was tired of the kind of jobs ex-yeomen were offered. He said he'd read a couple of my hairier-chested books, and did I have anything for him that would combine stenography with fishing and hunting and fresh air. I told him to come see me."

Alec swerved to avoid a head-on collision with a hot rod, and lit a cigarette from the dash lighter.

"It turned out fine all around. Luke had been Dear-Johned in the war, and evidently none of the local *ragazze* around Scranton, Pennsylvania, took his postwar fancy. I guess maybe he was sour on women, and very possibly sour on the peace. A chief yeoman on a ship or shore station had a lot of authority, and being a chief clerk ashore wouldn't appeal to a man who had run the inner workings of a carrier.

"So Luke lives here in Jersey with me most of the time. He's still a fast typist, even though his dictation is shaky. But he likes to chop wood and build fires and fish in the lake and, most important, he doesn't want to be an author. He can't cook very well, but you can live on spaghetti and meat-balls if you have to, and I'm a pretty fair chef myself in a simple sort of way, like steaks and scrambled eggs. I hope to

God he brings home a couple of new recipes, say like a good scallopine, from Mama and five sisters. But mainly between frozen foods and the canned stuff — God bless Chef Boy-Ar-Dee — we eat pretty good Wop fare."

"Seems a strange combination, a secretary-handyman-cook," Dinah said.

"Not so strange. Most Italians are raised in the kitchen. They don't see anything degrading about taking a turn at the skillet. They've been watching Mama back of the stove for most of their formative years."

"Well, I hope your paragon fetches you a fresh batch of recipes instead of bringing back a wife," Dinah said. "I'd hate to see any female intrusion into this all-boy paradise."

"No fear," Alec Barr said, turning off the main highway. "No bloody fear. If a wife comes in, out goes Luke, and Luke knows it."

"That's narrow of you," Dinah said. "Horrid old misanthrope."

"Golly, the country's lovely now," Penny said. "Look at those gorgeous trees. They're just turning."

They had come into a second-class road now, and it was closely rimmed with the crisping gold-and-red leaves of maple and beech against the deep backdrop of evergreen. Silver shafts of birch stood like bright palings among black-greenery, topped by the color-splotched canvas of the autumnal change. The air was growing colder, and the sun was painting the sky as it started to slide behind the swelling blue hills in the distance. In a few short minutes the change from grimy factory town and car-maggoty highway had been startling.

"That's why I love it," Alec said. "Two turns and you might as well be in Kenya. We'll be home in a few minutes."

"I hope so," Dinah said. "My old bones are beginning to chill."

He swerved the car into a graveled road. The road curved among the silver-glowing birch and a tumble of briared underbrush, with big pines and firs forming a canopy over the track. He squealed his tires as he achieved the summit, and drew up the Cadillac with a flourish behind a fieldstone house. The birch forest came almost into the graveled backyard.

"Home," he said, and went back to the trunk to retrieve the bags. "We go in the back way, like proper country folks. Enter through the kitchen, I always say, and see what kind of people live in the main house."

He unlocked a door and pressed a light switch. The kitchen seemed enormous, full of gleaming enameled dinosaurs.

"It's a do-it-yourself kitchen, all right," he said. "There's enough cubic feet in that deep freeze to store a couple of steers. Even an adult can cook on the stove, and we barbecue nearly everything outside, anyway. Come on into the headquarters. There'd better be a fire laid, or I'll skin me an Italian."

He plopped the bags at the side of a broad hall, which led into what at first appeared to be pure space overlooking a lake. But the space had a flagged floor, and a stone fireplace to the right, and constituted infinite space confined by two huge sheets of glass. The view was straight into the side of, and over, a mountain, with the sun-dyed blue sheen of a lake between. The drop from glass terrace to lake was sheer. A drained swimming pool lay level with the flagstones on the left, and the whole was confined again by the silver birch.

"My God!" Dinah said. "I thought I was going to step right out into the stratosphere! You've got yourself quite a view here, boy. How do you get down to the lake? Dive?"

Alec was stooping, lighting the birch fire. He looked over his shoulder.

"Easy enough. You can't see it from this particular promontory, but the slope to the right is really very gentle, and the view less stark from the other rooms. Except, of course, upstairs. I built this place kind of on a tilt."

He straightened up as the curled parchment bark of the logs began to crackle.

"That'll fry us in a moment. I got a thermostat for real winter, but I hate that kind of heat when I can get enough warmth out of a fireplace. We eat out here a lot. It collects an awful lot of sun in the wintertime. Now, the bar."

He turned his back on the view and walked over to a long oaken slab, mounted on a cabinet that occupied half the walled end of the room. One game head, a black-maned animal with an arched neck and long back-curved horns, looked arrogantly out at a corner of the lake.

"What's that thing?" Dinah asked. "A moose?"

"No, it's not a moose. It's a sable."

"Oh," Penny said. "That's what they make those lovely coats out of!"

"I'm afraid not." Alec smiled. He had been subjected to that assumption several hundred times. "What they make those lovely coats out of is a kind of black weasel that runs around loose in Russia. This is an African sable antelope, and it's called sable only because it's black."

He was behind the bar now, standing in front of a bright array of bottles and glassware on shelves behind him.

"What'll it be for two cold girls?"

"Anything with gin," Dinah said. "A Gibson be too much trouble?"

"Not if you can wait a second for the ice," Alec said, and disappeared into the kitchen. He returned with a bleeding finger and a zinc airlines bucket, which he plumped into a hole in the bar top. He sucked at the bleeding finger.

"Been a long time since anybody defrosted anything around here," he said. "Luke told that idiot in the village to look in once a week. I guess he's drunk."

"You want a Band-Aid for that finger? I suppose you've got them under the bar too." Dinah tasted her drink. "You make a powerful Gibson, man. Cheers." She walked over to the fire and lifted the back of her skirt against the blaze, which was now beginning to leap. "I don't know why a girl always gets colder back there than anywhere else, but it's a matter of scientific fact."

"When you've thawed out a bit, I'll show you the rest of the joint, and also your quarters," Alec said. "Meanwhile, look!" He pointed a finger at the far shore of the lake. Five deer, three does and a couple of yearlings, were tiptoeing daintily down to drink. Simultaneously, an echelon of black ducks flighted in and splashed hard as their undercarriages hit the water.

"That's what I mean about this place," he said. "It's still real country."

"Doesn't shooting them scare them off?" Penny asked.

"We don't shoot around this lake. There's plenty of deer

— too damned many — within a mile or so, and we only shoot the transient ducks off the ponds back there."

"I must say it's beautiful," Dinah said. "You'd think you were a million miles away from Times Square."

The ceiling in the next room was lofty, the room's dimensions vast. An enormous desk occupied one corner of the room, which elled off to still another room.

"My God, is this where all the old elephants come to die?" Dinah said. "Penny, we're lost in a zoo."

Alec looked a little rueful.

"I'm sort of fond of my pets," he said. "That lion was a personal friend of mine. That elephant" — he pointed to two enormous ivory curves to the left of the fireplace — "that elephant I spent the best part of two months chasing. And that tiger" — he jerked a thumb at the monstrous striped beast over the fireplace — "just about cost me my neck. But they sort of soothe me. At least they don't remind me of editors and agents and traffic jams."

"Did you really shoot all these animals yourself?" Penny's voice was a little awed. "Like those great big ugly things on the other wall? Weren't you scared to death?"

"I suppose I was, at the time, particularly with those great big black things. They're called Cape buffalo. But mostly you're excited first and frightened afterward. I remember after I shot that lion I threw up behind a bush."

"I'd have thrown up before I shot that lion," Dinah muttered. "Can you really live comfortably with all these things you've — shall we say deprived of freedom and the pursuit of happiness?"

"You'd be surprised how comfortably I can live with

them. They grow on you. And if it's any consolation, most of them would have been dead pretty soon, anyhow. They're all old males, well past breeding, kicked out of the tribe, and subject to all the ills old people contract for." His voice had suddenly become a little impatient.

Alec swept them to a seat on a circular green sofa before the fire and sat across the circular coffee table, a brass-studded wooden Arab brazier. He placed his drink on the edge. There was an awkward pause, the first in a delightful day.

"Excuse, please," said Dinah. "Didn't mean to be rude. Could I have a little more of this deelicious gin, please, and then could I see the rest of your castle?"

"You're forgiven," Alec said, heading out to the bar. He jerked his head over one shoulder, pointing with his chin.

"The girls' room is there, but I'm afraid you'll find a warthog glaring at you if you use that one. If you're sensitive to warthogs there's another john just off the next hall, to your right. No warthogs."

Mother looked at daughter.

"I think we stepped on a corn," she said.

"I think you were pretty horrid," Penny said. "He's so proud of his house — and I think, lonely in it, in spite of all that talk about this Luke person."

"We'll try to make it up to him," Dinah said.

No wonder his wife stays in town, Dinah thought, as Alec led her to the double-bedded guest room, which supported still another spotted creature — a jaguar — snarling from the wall. I'll have nightmares all night.

"Does Lassie up there bite?" she asked, indicating the big cat. "Does a gun go with the bedside paraphernalia?"

"All right, kid me." Alec was good-natured about it. "So I'm not but fourteen years old. But the point is, I like it, and can work in it. The fireplaces draw and the ashtrays are big enough. It's my kind of house — not that fancy-schmancy Park Avenue stuff."

"I think it's a wonderful house," Penny said with startling vehemence, causing her mother to stare at her quizzically. "I think it's a marvelous house."

"Of course it's a marvelous house," Dinah said. "But I've known Alec so long he'd think it was very strange if I suddenly drowned him in flattery."

"Correct," Alec said. "Now, if you ladies want to tidy up a bit, I'll go down and cope with the steaks. Charcoal takes a little time. Don't hurry; there's a hi-fi arrangement in that Arab chest in the big room, and you know the way to the bar now. Make yourself easy until I yell."

"Couldn't I set a table or something?" Penny asked.

"That would be nice. We'll eat off the big table in the patio room. The stars look pretty through the glass. You'll find all the necessities in the big cupboard in the kitchen."

Alec went whistling downstairs to see to his charcoal. Dinah Lawrence looked curiously at her daughter again.

"What are you doing, chum, bucking for Luke's job or something?"

"I'm not bucking for Luke's job. I just don't think you ought to tease him so much. He loves this place, and you're making fun of it. I'll bet — I'll bet —"

"You'll bet what, honey?"

((*213*))

"I'll bet that his wife spoiled it for him and that's why he left her."

"What do you know about Alec leaving his wife?" Dinah's voice sharpened. "I never mentioned it. She's just in Europe, far as I know."

"I heard it in the ladies' room in Twenty-One. Somebody saying — just as you left — something like, 'Well, I see old Alec's cutting up high and handsome since he walked out on Amelia. First it was that Bayne broad and now he's got two summer replacements, mother and daughter.' "

Dinah Lawrence prodded her daughter's shoulder.

"Look, Junior," she said. "Whatever the reason for Alec Barr's leaving Amelia, it didn't have anything to do with her lack of appreciation for this hunting-camp retreat. And don't pay too much attention to the things you hear in ladies' rooms. Mostly they're a flock of lies."

"It didn't sound to me like a flock of lies. It sounded like a flock of truth. And you're in love with Alec, aren't you? You always have been, haven't you? And he's always cheated on his wife, hasn't he? And you've slept together, haven't —"

Dinah Lawrence slapped her daughter, hard.

Penny Lawrence pressed her hand against her cheek, and her eyes were huge and hurt.

"You shouldn't have done that," she said after a moment. "I won't forget it. You really shouldn't have. I'm a woman, not a child."

"You're not too much of a woman to get smacked for being rude and childish and way out of line." Dinah Lawrence made her voice flat and cold. "You've got half a crush on a man old enough to be your father, and you're stumbling around like a puppy. What I feel for Alec Barr is nobody's business. Particularly it's none of your business, and I'll thank you to mind what few manners I've taught you. That clear?"

"That is very clear. And it only confirms what I was saying."

Penny's voice was equally flat and cold. Her eyes were very bright, and free of tears. "And don't you ever slap me again, do you hear?"

Dinah shook her head and ran fingers through her hair.

"I'm sorry, baby," she said. "Really sorry. There are some things. . . ."

"All right," her daughter said. "We'll forget it. But don't call me baby."

The dinner had not been a total disaster. Alec had exhumed some frozen corncobs, which he had managed to roast without charring too much, and with the help of a few more packets of quick-frozen garden products had contrived a meal of which he was quite proud. The steak was only a little bit scorched on the outside, and only a touch blue and mildly clammy in the middle.

They drowsed from the fire and the keen country air, and went early off to bed, sleeping late into the morning. When Dinah and Penny came downstairs, Alec was bustling, whistling happily. He had already laid the table for breakfast.

"Look at that day!" he said, indicating a flawless autumn sky and a vulgar excess of golden sunshine. The light had flooded the closed patio, and he had opened one door leading out to the flagged terrace. "How'd you sleep?"

"Died," Dinah Lawrence said. "And Lassie didn't bite me even once. I must say there's something to be said for gin and that gorgeous red wine. What is our host preparing for breakfast, might I ask?"

"First, a covey of Scotch sours, if that pleases you, and then waffles and hard ham from Virginia. There are some English muffins and some fine fresh canned fruit. That's about the best I can do at the moment."

"Lead us to those sours," Dinah said. "Do you think we're making a drunkard out of Penny?"

"Hell, I was drinking corn likker out of Dixie cups when I was fifteen," Alec said. "And it never stunted my growth any. And we'll all be on the wagon tomorrow — or at least Tuesday. How do they taste?"

"You have unforeseen talents, Barr," Dinah said. "I never knew you were a housewife before. I do believe you actually adore this boy-scouting."

"I must confess to it. Give me a good piece of meat to ruin and blow some smoke in my eyes, drop a lot of sand in the soup, and I'm as merry as a bird. Come on now, Di, it's about time to activate the waffle iron. Penny, you're in charge of the coffee detail, and I shall fry the ham."

After breakfast, over a third cup of coffee, Alec said:

"While I was stirring around among the papers, waiting for you two slugs-abed to arise, a thought hit me. Penny, seeing as how your mother and I are both writing books, a dreary business at best, why don't you persuade your ma to move out here with me? We're amply chaperoned, for Luke'll be back tomorrow or next day. No, wait a minute —" Dinah Lawrence had started to speak.

"Hear me out. It makes sense. No noise, no telephones, a hell of a reference library — we'll set up your mill in the reference library, Di — a built-in secretary for the recopying, and somebody to talk to when the day's work's done. Also somebody to try out ideas on. It's lonesome as hell working in a city apartment, and always tempting to drop into Tim's or P.J.'s for a drink when you should be pounding that machine. What do you think, Pen?"

"I think it's a simply marvelous idea." Penny's voice was cold as she turned to her mother. "After all, it's your first book, Mother, and Alec's had so much experience and it's so quiet and I'm sure Luke is a lot better cook than Alec said."

Dinah Lawrence raised her hand.

"Whoa," she said. "Whoa right up. Just a minute. Apart from the dubious propriety of my moving into the country with a married man, there never was a house big enough for two writers. I think we've been over that route before. You write your book and I'll write mine — both in our own quiet corners. We've been friends a long time, Alec. I'd like to keep it that way."

"But Mother, Alec only wants to help you."

"Forget it. I know what I'm talking about. We'd be at each other's throats in three days, if not less." Dinah fixed her daughter with a stare.

Alec shrugged, looking disappointed.

"It was just an idea. I thought —"

"It was a fine and generous and entirely impractical idea, but no dice. Penny, you've more to pack than me. Why don't you throw your things into the bag, so we won't have to rush for that airplane?"

"Yes, Mother," Penny said in a small voice.

"What's wrong between you and Penny?" Alec asked, after Penny disappeared.

"Nothing very much. Slight mother-daughter tiff. It'll pass. Ignore it."

Alec shrugged. "Women," he said, "of all ages."

They drove slowly through the burnished autumn afternoon to Newark Airport, subdued as people are when the weekend is over and one is to leave the others behind. Alec flicked on the radio again, with the crack that "now is the time to hear an announcement about another Pearl Harbor," and was withered by both women. He chopped off the station and drove in silence.

Am I going to ask Amelia for a divorce? His mind roved. It's a hell of a lot of trouble, and damned expensive as well. She's done nothing really to deserve it. I'm the bastard in the basement. If I do divorce her, what do I find that's better? There's the work to be done, and you sure as hell can't work when you're separating the silver and dividing up the books.

If only I were actually desperately acutely in love with someone. Dinah's wonderful, but Dinah sees me all too clearly. There's no use building a new trap that I'll only be running away from, cheating — lousy word, cheating — as soon as I get bored and fiddle-footed. He sighed deeply.

"What's the matter?" Dinah Lawrence asked. "That one really came out of your boots."

"Nothing. Not really. I'm just feeling despondent about tomorrow. Work and wagon and harsh reality. The honeymoon's over."

"Honeymoon, how?" Penny asked him. Her voice was still very small.

"Not exactly a honeymoon, sweetie," Alec said. "Say a vacation from responsibility. The time has come for nose and grindstone to merge, and it makes me sad. For a little while this summer I thought I was young. It's a mistake all of us old fellows make. When are you coming home again?" He spoke suddenly, brightly.

"Thanksgiving, I guess."

"Well, unless your ma's so deep in her book as to be impossible, let's all get gussied up and misbehave outrageously one night. By Thanksgiving I'll need a break. We'll eat some caviar and hear some jazz and kick over an ashcan and paint the town bright red."

"It sounds wonderful, if Mother isn't too busy. And thanks for a lovely weekend, Alec. I truly love your house, and hope you'll let me come back."

"Thanks, Pen. Incidentally, have you read that last book of mine, that *Total Loss* thing?"

"No, I'm ashamed to say I haven't —"

"Figured. If you'll reach into the glove compartment, you'll find one. It'll give you something to read on the plane. It's handwrit in, but don't show your ma. Wait until you get on the plane before you flip to the flyleaf."

"Golly, thanks, Alec. And I won't show my mother. She'd only be jealous."

"I doubt if a simple signature can stir the modern female to jealousy." Alec smiled. "Anyhow, it was fun playing with you. I'll just let your mother see you off." He drew up to the unloading stand, and beckoned a porter. " 'Bye, sweetie, and thanks."

Penny got out of the car, came round to the driver's side, and kissed Alec on the cheek. She whispered:

"If you'd made me the same offer you made my mother I'd have taken you up on it."

Sheila—The Girl
You Fall in Love with in Wartime

London, charred and scarred and bomb-pitted, blacked-out and hell-dark by night, beset by shortages and austere to the point of starvation, slave to the queue and the ration book, still had an almost violent gaiety. There seemed to be a total absence of fear, and the bravery was not bravado.

London, was — well, chirpily cheerful by day and riotous at night. By day the parks, Green and Hyde, were blanketed by home-leave soldiers making love to their girls under newspapers. By night, in the bars and private drinking clubs and sly-groggeries, the roof was an introduction. You walked into the "American" bar in any major hotel, nodded at a lady, and left shortly thereafter for your digs or hers. She might have been a duchess or a tart.

Alec continued to feel the strange exultation of war. America, safe beyond the sea, could know nothing of this feeling, of bombs or bombings, of submarines and sinking ships, of this kind of — well, friendship, fellowship — that war engendered. Polish fliers, RAF types with sweeping moustaches, bearded naval types, WAAFs, WRENs, ATS and ATC girls — girls from Ireland and Scotland and Wales who had come in to work for this ministry or that and who were out on the razzle after working hours — all drank and danced and freely fornicated out of war's peculiar friendship.

There was some resentment of the growing number of enlisted American personnel who crowded the pubs and out-bought the poorly paid local soldiery for the favors of the local lassies, but that was mainly confined to the outlying county towns. In London everyone was nearly on his own, on equal footing, except that the officers kept mainly to their own terrain, while the enlisted men worked the enlisted ranks of the ladies, apart from the tarts around Piccadilly and in the Strand, on Curzon Street and along the Mall.

With such a profusion of femininity, it was unusual that Alec did not meet Sheila Aubrey in The Deanery or at Sandy's or in one of the cocktail lounges.

He met her as he ducked hurriedly into a doorway when the Luftwaffe launched the first massive wave of the Second Blitz, three days after Alec had nursed his convoy up the Estuary.

She was remarkably pretty, Alec thought. Black hair crisp and curly, snug to her head, eyes almost purple in their blueness, milky skin and body full in the greatcoat over long, slim legs. Irish for sure, he thought as she followed him behind the heavy felt curtain.

He took out a package of cigarettes and shook it at her.

"Smoke?" he said. "This ought to be over pretty soon."

"Thank you." She looked at him levelly. "I don't think it'll be over pretty soon. Not from the sound of it." She accepted a light. "This sounds like it might well be a big one. I'd almost forgotten what it was like."

"I wouldn't know," Alec said. "It's my first. But I'm afraid it's also partially my fault."

She looked at him through the smoke and raised an eyebrow.

"How could it possibly be your fault?" Another big-mouth Yank. In a minute he'll make a pass at me. Blackout makes the whole world kin.

"Well, I didn't exactly order it from Berlin," Alec shouted over the ack-ack. "But I sort of brought a convoy up the Estuary the other day, and I suppose Jerry got wind of it. I've been told you've had quite a holiday from our friends upstairs until now. Perhaps this little visit is a gesture of discouragement for future naval activities of my sort."

"They do have quite an intelligence setup," she shouted back, smiling now. "Thank you so much for livening things up for us. I'm afraid we were growing soft — and the weather's been so lovely lately, you'd scarcely know there was a war on if you didn't listen to the BBC."

"My name is Alec" — the rest of his words were drowned as a bomb struck nearby and the building trembled. There was a crash of glass. The drone of motors, uplift by the thunder-rattle of antiaircraft batteries, made him shout — "Barr!"

"How do you" — there was another tremendous explosion on the other side and increased intensity of ground fire — "do," she shouted. "We're lucky for tonight. They won't drop another in the same neighborhood. I'm Sheila" — another tremendous explosion rocked the building again — "Aubrey!"

"Your intelligence is all wet," Alec shouted. "Lightning does strike twice in the same —" Still another explosion. "Somebody up there is looking for us. What did you say the name was?"

"Aubrey. Sheila Aubrey," the girl shouted. "Listen." There was a lessening thrum of motors overhead. "Our chaps have them on the run. They really shouldn't have given us a chance to mend our fences. You'll hear the all clear in a moment. See? The ack-ack's dying."

In a few minutes the all-clear siren wailed.

"That's all for tonight," the girl said. "Home to beddy-bye for me. I get up early in the morning. The Air Ministry needs me. So nice to have met you, Lieutenant — you said Barr? Even if you did bring this revisitation on our heads."

Alec glanced at his watch.

"It's very early yet. I don't suppose I could interest you in a drink and perhaps a bite of supper? I've done all the damage I'm capable of for one evening." He smiled shyly. "I'm rather short on companionship in this big town. New boy."

The girl looked at him coolly, appraisingly, seemingly conducting a short argument with herself, and then nodded.

"I suppose. You don't really look like that kind of Yank. I don't mean to be rude," she said hurriedly, "but I —"

"I think I know what you mean," Alec said, taking her elbow as they stepped out into the street. "Overfed, over-sexed, and over here. I don't bite. And I'm also a happily married man, if that means anything. We're not too far from a place called The Deanery, where quite a few of my State-side chums hang out — newspaper people, correspondents, radio types, like that. Or we might, a little later, be able to snag a taxi for the Savoy."

"Not tonight we won't be able to snag a taxi for the Savoy," she said. "Look at that. But The Deanery is just fine. I live a few blocks away, in Hill Street. It's walkable."

The Deanery was crowded, smoke-filled, noisy, bar-jammed, tables filled, wild with the hysterical exhilaration that follows air raids in which you don't get killed. Half of London seemed to have used it as an air-raid shelter. All the press corps, it seemed, had been drinking at The Deanery when the first wave of bombers came over.

"This is no good," Alec said. "Perhaps we'd better try the Grosvenor or the Dorchester."

"They won't be any better, not tonight," Sheila Aubrey said. "See here. Working at the Air Ministry entails a few perks. I'm just a hop and a skip away. I've a tiny flat with a few rather illegal things in the fridge. If you'd like — only thing is I've no grog, except possibly a little sherry."

"That I can fix with my vulgar American money," Alec said, and fought his way to the bar, where he importuned the bartender. The bartender nodded negatively and then changed the nod to a smile, beckoning to Alec to follow him in the general direction of the WC. A moment later Alec emerged with a slightly bulging jacket.

"Let's go," he said. "Home to Hill Street." He gurgled slightly as he walked.

The flat was tiny: one small bedroom, a slightly larger lounge, a gas-ring-*cum*-refrigerator kitchen in an alcove, and a bath in which one might reach everything from any given position. But it was bright and cheerfully chintzy behind the heavy blackout drapes, and there were daffodils on a small coffee table in front of a burnt-orange sofa. Alec set a bottle of Scotch on the coffee table.

"It's probably homemade," he said. "But this is the best I could do. At that place. At this hour."

"It's a miracle," she said. "That's the first full bottle of

private whiskey I've seen since the war started — or almost."
She slipped out of her coat, and took it to the bedroom. "It's
not very large," she said. "But at least I don't have to share
it. There's only room in the bath for one pair of stockings at
a time. There should be one tiny ice tray in the fridge if you
like ice in your whiskey, as I'm told most Americans do."

"I can take it or leave it," Alec said. "In this instance I'll
take it. You?"

"Just with a spot of soda. I like it warm. I'll be with you in
a moment. While you're seeing to the ice, you might check
what's in the larder. There should be some cheese and biscuits and possibly some sausage. Or I can make you an egg;
yesterday was ration day. Certainly there's Spam, courtesy of
your people."

"Sounds like a feast," Alec said. "I'm one of the few mem-
bers of the military who actually likes Spam. Hell's horns,
woman, you've got kippers and sardines as well. You must be
running a black market."

"A girl does the best she can," Sheila Aubrey said, coming
out of the bedroom. She had done something to the black
curls, had freshened her lipstick, and was wearing a simple
jersey over a tweed skirt. The jersey showed curves that had
been hinted but not verified.

"Tell me about you," Alec said when they sat with their
drinks.

"Simple. Born Irish. Raised British. I was orphaned early
— father in the IRA business, mother of heartbreak, I
should suppose. A sort of renegade aunt sent for me and I
grew up in Sussex, hence no Irish accent. Went to school
until the war came, and then I went to work. I didn't fancy

uniforms very much — I mean I couldn't see being a WREN or a Fannie — so I got a job in the ministry. That's about it."

"That's all of it?"

"Well, there was a fiancé, sort of." Sheila Aubrey poked a thumb at the sky. "RAF type. Didn't come back one day. Nothing much since but work. I decided early on not to become a member of the officers' mess. Not that it's easy these days, with everybody hurling themselves into bed after one cocktail. . . ."

"It would be difficult to resist the impulse to attempt to hurl you," Alec said, and held up a hand. "Have no fear. I appreciate the hospitality and shall not presume."

"If I thought you might I wouldn't have brought you home," Sheila Aubrey said. "It's the only home I've got. My aunt rather unfortunately got bombed out. What about you?"

"Writing type," Alec said, adopting her clipped phrasing. "Moderately successful. Married. Childless. That's about it."

"What kind of writing?"

"Newspapers first. Then articles for magazines. Then books. Most recently a play. It was still running when I left."

He lit two cigarettes and passed her one.

"Thank you. What is the play called?"

"*Not Without Laughter*. Not a very good play, I'm afraid. But very commercial."

She frowned.

"I've read about the play, and I think I've read a book of yours. If you're that Barr, what are you doing in a Navy uniform? Why aren't you a war correspondent? Or, if you're married, why didn't you just stay home? I believe they defer married men over there."

Alec laughed and tipped another inch of Scotch into each glass.

"I didn't want to miss it. I wanted to be the first Barr actually to go to war. Grandpa contrived to get captured by the Yankees early, and my father caught the flu about the time World War I ended. I wanted to be a reluctant hero and see it from the inside."

"You're putting me on," she said. "I can't believe —" And then the alert screamed again outside, and the thrumming was heard again.

"Oh, God, they're back," she shouted above the uproar. "I thought they were gone for good tonight. I don't mind it once, but twice —"

Alec saw her shaking, and put an arm gently round her shoulders.

"Shush," he said, in a kindly roar. "They'll be gone again soon. And we've had our near misses for tonight. At least this is —" Another bomb drowned his voice.

". . . what?"

"A better bomb shelter than that doorway. We've got whiskey and lights inside and the percentages with us."

After the all clear Sheila Aubrey said:

"I don't really mean to be a ninny. But it does get on one's nerves. I mean, after it's happened often enough, and the windows blow out, and the lights go, and there's always a great hole where something familiar has been —" She was still trembling.

"Stop it, I'll have a look outside." He put out the lights, drew back the blackout curtains, and gazed at the night. Half of London seemed ablaze.

"It was pretty bad," he said soberly. "I'll have to wait, I imagine, before I can start beating my way back to the Savoy. Until the streets clear a bit, anyhow, and the fire brigade does its chores."

"You can't go back to the Savoy tonight," Sheila Aubrey said. "It's too far to walk. You'll have to stay here. And anyhow I want you to stay here — I don't want to be alone tonight. And I don't mean what you think I mean. I don't — I mean . . ."

Alec smiled.

"I know what you mean. And I know you don't. Sure, I'll stay, and gratefully. I'll just curl up on the divan and sweat out the dawn. Or we can both sit up and talk until morning."

Sheila turned and kissed him lightly on the cheek. She smiled mistily.

"It's not that I would actually mind so very much, but tonight, I — I just want someone near me without — I want to be held without —"

"I'll hold you, without repeat without," Alec Barr said. "On that you can depend."

Alec Barr lay in bed, his left arm cramped by the head that nestled into his shoulder, afraid to move for fear of waking the girl who now was sleeping sweetly. He was wearing skivvies; the girl was wearing pajamas. She was very soft and fragrant as she breathed evenly beside him.

Alec Barr looked at the ceiling, considered his benumbed

arm, and smiled wryly. He had stroked her into slumber as one might gentle a horse or a child. He shook his head slightly.

Of all the women in London you might go to bed with, he thought, the sailor fresh from the sea has to wind up with a platonic roommate. Here I lie abed with a beautiful girl I've not so much as kissed. Amelia would never believe it. He dozed lightly before he was wakened by a slight touch on the shoulder.

"There's tea, if you'd like some," Sheila said, coming back into the room in a dressing gown. "Did you sleep at all? And I'm sorry I was such a mess last night. But thank you, Alec. Thanks terribly."

Alec scrubbed the back of his hand across his face. His mouth was dry and gummy.

"Slept like a log," he lied. "And no thanks necessary. You wouldn't have such a thing as a razor handy, would you? I hate to walk into the Savoy, if it's still standing, with a green beard like this one. Navy regs and all that."

"I would indeed," she said. "And also the egg we didn't eat last night."

"There were quite a lot of things we didn't do last night," Alec said, getting into his pants. "It was sort of an unusual night."

Sheila Aubrey smiled and wrinkled her nose.

"I'm quite free this evening if you have nothing better to do," she said. "I'm off early. Fiveish."

"I have nothing better to do I wouldn't cancel. Meet me at the Savoy — in the bar?"

"Love to," she said, and kissed him briefly on the cheek as he went out the door to search for a cab.

Alec logged in later with naval headquarters and was informed that his ship had taken a hit in last night's bombing. Nothing really severe, but troublous enough to warrant the attention of the commanding officer. The number-one stern gun was loose from its moorings, and a couple of Oerlikons were past redemption. There was some damage below decks. It would be appreciated if —

Alec was driven down to the East End by another mousily anonymous female driver to find a British repair crew already busy with blowtorches and welding apparatus. Four P.M. still saw him busy. He went ashore and rang up the Air Ministry, and was eventually put through to a Miss Aubrey in Coding.

"I'm dreadfully sorry," he said. "But I'm afraid our Savoy date is off. My old bucket took a little beating from that business last night, and I'm up to my ears with your countrymen, who seem to want to work around the clock. There's some damage down below that can be repaired at night — damage that'll prevent discharge unless it's fixed fast, and we are aiming for a speedy turnaround. Sorry. Maybe tomorrow?"

"Tomorrow's fine," Sheila Aubrey said. "But I've a better idea. If you finish any time before midnight, why don't you come round to the flat and we'll have another quiet evening. Maybe we won't even have to shout. There's still some of your whiskey left."

"Lovely. If I can possibly wind up here, you'll find me knocking on your door."

Alec got out of his working khaki at eight P.M., and whistled while he shaved carefully again and flicked a quick brush over his blues. You had to hand it to the Limeys, he thought. They had accomplished in a day what it would take a week to do in Hampton Roads back in the States. The battered old bucket had been welded back as good as — or possibly better than — new. Maybe the Blitz had taught the Limeys how to turn to and get things done in a hurry — the air-raid wardens, the fire-brigade boys, the bomb-disposal squads. He whistled. Here it was only just past eight and with luck he'd be back in the West End by nine. If he were just lucky enough to find a taxi. . . .

The evening promised much. What a lovely girl, this Sheila, whom he'd met in the doorway — what a beautiful girl, what a nice girl, what a sweet girl — and after his exemplary behavior of last night, what a gorgeous promise of things, more serious things, to come. He whistled and silently applauded himself for taking no advantage of proximity last night. When the moment came it would come, with full eagerness on both sides, because time was short and she knew time was short, that he'd be shipping out again in a week or less.

Sheila was no tart, no military mattressback, like the easy ones he'd seen in the hotels and bars and clubs. But at the same time she was all woman — she'd been engaged and semiwidowed in wartime, and she knew the briefness of time in war. There was no thought of Amelia, of infidelity, here. This was wartime in London. There were submarines beneath the sea and aircraft overhead. Time was short, and time was also sweet. And tonight Sheila would come as sweetly into his arms. And not merely for comfort, like a child in the dark.

God smiled. Alec walked off the docks and beheld a taxi. The cabbie was agreeable, he was going back to the West End anyhow.

"Took a proper pounding, we did, last night," the hacker said almost with pride. "Where to, Guy?"

"Hill Street," Alec said. "And step on it as much as you can. I've got a lovely lady waiting."

"Too right, Guy," the hacker said, and winked. "Nuffink like a war for lovely lydies, eh?"

"Too right," Alec said shortly, and settled back in the corner of the cab to meditate on fate and blackouts and air raids and doorways and lovely girls named Sheila.

They were coming into Grosvenor Square when the air-raid siren went.

"Cor," the driver said. " 'E's back agyne. I can just get you to Grosvenor 'Ouse, unless you want a shelter?"

"Make it Grosvenor House," Alec said. "Damn it to hell. In another five minutes I'd have been at Sheila's. Well, I can beat it over there after the all clear."

"Wot was that?" the driver asked, as the thrumming grew and the antiaircraft began to bark in the distance.

"Nothing," Alec said. "Step on it."

The driver drew up in front of Grosvenor House. Alec paid him and dashed inside. The lobby was jammed, and so was the American Bar downstairs, but he managed to wriggle through to the bar and extract a large Scotch from the bartender.

Jerry was over in force tonight, and he seemed to have abandoned the dock area for a repeat run on the West End. The crump of big bombs rattled the windows. Once the hotel appeared to have been straddled — how close, it was difficult to say. The ack-ack batteries in Hyde and Green parks rattled your teeth as well as the windows, and you could hear the scream of the Spitfires over the steady thrumming of the big bombers. After half an hour the thrumming died again, as on the night before, and the ack-ack faded as the Nazi striking force headed back to Holland.

"Nasty one, that," the man next to Alec said. "I don't mind it so long as they concentrate on the docks. It's when they plonk one straight down on the Café de Paris that a bloke feels uncomfortable. Bastards have no class consciousness. That's the trouble with the Hun."

When the all clear sounded Alec stepped out into the night again, and once more found London stabbed and ringed round with fire. Ambulances screamed, and the rescue-and-fire teams were already at work.

He picked his way through rubble in the general direction of Hill Street, uncertain still of London topography, and after several blocks concluded that he was lost. But no — the fires were bright enough for him to pick out a sign, Hill Street. He recognized the corner.

His feet carried him numbly in the direction they'd taken last night, in the dark, and suddenly his stomach twisted.

There was no bell to ring.

There was no door for him to knock on.

There was no house behind the door.

There was no girl in the house that was not behind the door that had no bell for him to ring.

There was no girl. There would never be a girl — not that girl.

ABOUT THE AUTHOR

Robert Chester Ruark was forty-nine years old
when he died in 1965. Into that comparatively
short span he had packed a lot of life.

During his early years in North Carolina,
despite a certain need for frugal living
on the part of his family, he inherited two
assets that were later to contribute in a major
way to his success as a writer. His father owned
a large private library, and the boy developed
and was able to satisfy a limitless curiosity
about books. Also there was his grandfather,
who knew about guns and hunting and, better still,
was able to pass on his skills to the youngster
who wanted to learn.

Between these two, Ruark acquired an education
beyond his school textbook learning. He was
only fifteen when he enrolled at the University
of North Carolina. While he studied journalism
there he also worked on a local paper as editor,
reporter, advertising manager and subscription
salesman for ten dollars a week. Those were
the depression years. He went through college
on one suit and two pairs of shoes.

In the five years or so between graduation
in 1935 and the war, he worked on various papers
in Washington, beginning as a copyboy and rising
to sportswriter for twenty-five dollars a week.

In World War II he served as commander of armed
guards on munition ships in the North Atlantic and
the Mediterranean. He wrote successfully about
the war for magazines in the United States, and
when he discarded his uniform Scripps-Howard hired
him as a reporter and, subsequently, columnist.

In this capacity, he traveled all over
the world and found material enough to write eight
highly successful books. His first,
Grenadine Etching, appeared in 1947. His intimate
knowledge of Africa and his prowess as a white
hunter inspired *Horn of the Hunter, Something of Value,*
and *Uhuru.*

He might never have hunted big game had it not
been for his grandfather, the protagonist of
The Old Man and the Boy and *The Old Man's Boy Grows
Older.* His *Poor No More* told
the stark tale, in the light of experience,
of an impoverished young man's growth through
the lean college years to success. His last
novel, *The Honey Badger,* was published
posthumously in 1965. In the fall of 1966 The New
American Library published the best of Ruark's hunting
writing under the title *Use Enough Gun.*

From London, where he died, Ruark was brought
for burial to the little town of Palamós, on
the Costa Brava, in Spain, where he had become
a doyen of the local community in the fifteen years
he lived there.